Preface

Shortly after the practical use of electricity was discovered, it was learned also that the simple make-and-break of an electric circuit wired to an alarm of some sort—bell or buzzer—could make for a usable intrusion indicator. Necessity is indeed the mother of invention, and the race was on! The basic burglar alarm of the past consisted of two metal contacts, one in the window frame, the other in the sash. When you slid the window open, the contacts touched and the bell rang. Out would come the irate homeowner with shotgun or putter, whichever was most convenient. The basic burglar found that the easiest way to circumvent this sort of an alarm was to simply smash the window. So a new system was developed using conductive metal tapes right on the glass. When you break the glass, you break the tape, the relay drops, and the alarm goes off. That circumvented the window-breaking burglar! Technology has evolved by leaps and bounds—on both sides. And as new techniques for foiling would-be thieves have been developed, the thieves have contrived countermeasures. More valuable possessions require more sophisticated devices, and these have been countered by more sophisticated burglars. It is a rip-roaring battle royal with all the intrigue of a James Bond novel.

We have systems today that you wouldn't have believed possible ten years ago. Let something go amiss, and one system will actually dial your telephone (or the police precinct number) and deliver a verbal message when the phone is answered! Let an intruder enter a protected area and alarms will sound locally or remotely, and photographs can be taken of the intruder without his knowledge.

There's an amusing story about the chief engineer in Brighton, England, who had a telephone warning repeater wired to his flat in the city. Should the power fail for any reason, the device would dial his home telephone number. When he lifted the receiver, the message would come through loud and clear "The power has failed." Secure in the knowledge that he had thus protected his equipment, he proceeded to forget about the system. In fact, he even forgot about it when he moved and had his phone number changed. Shortly thereafter, the equipment **did** fail, and the repeater promptly dialed his number. For the rest of the evening, the repeater at the power station stated, "The power has failed," while the telephone equipment at central said "The number you have dialed is not a working number."

It wasn't long before man realized that such systems consist of a series of component parts. There are detecting devices, suitable circuitry to sense a change of state in the detector, and alarm systems used to provide a suitable action when a change is sensed. By combining suitable detectors with suitable circuitry and suitable alarms, you can protect almost anything from almost anybody. It becomes a function of the value of what you want to protect, and the risk of the loss thereof.

While intrusion alarm systems are the queens of the May, it is a short step to incorporating other alarms as well—principally, a fire alarm system that can provide ample warning of the presence of fire, or in some installations, even trigger the extinguishing machinery into operation to contain a blaze, or at least help the fire department get a good start on so doing.

Naturally, as the sophistication factor grows, the maintenance and sales and servicing problems increase as well. It takes more than a guy with a screwdriver in his pocket to make an installation these days. And your local friendly TV technician can't do more than scratch his head over some of the fancy microwave circuitry being used today. So, there's a new breed of technician in this business. He has a devious mind that anticipates everything that can happen. He's as wily as a two-dollar lawyer fixing a traffic ticket. He has the understanding and sympathy of your local psychiatrist. And he's a salesman, too. But mostly, he's a technician with an understanding of how electronic things work, with a constant drive to stay right on top of what's new in his field. And that's why this book is being written.

Take a long look at what's happening around you. People have bigger and more expensive cars, fancier stereo equipment, fine color television receivers, furs, jewelry, cameras, firearms, everything that's easily negotiable to the right people. Naturally, they want to protect these things. They want to protect them from the people who want to take them away. We don't mean to get into social problems here, but they are a necessary aspect of life in our society. The drug addict with a $50 a day habit can't earn enough from a work-a-day job to support himself and his habit, so he resorts to theft as a way

No. 556
$7.95

FIRE & THEFT

SECURITY SYSTEMS

By Byron Wels

TAB BOOKS
Blue Ridge Summit, Pa. 17214

FIRST EDITION

FIRST PRINTING—JUNE 1971
SECOND PRINTING—FEBRUARY 1972

Library of Congress Card Number: 77-155977

of earning money for his drugs. And, there are others who, for one reason or another, resort to theft.

Thus, people are frightened; they want protection. Find the right protective system for the right people, install and test it properly, instruct the owner in how it works and how to use it, and you'll have a friend and customer for a good long time. Periodic service checks at moderate fees can be yours as well. But before we start servicing, it helps to know how various systems work and what they're designed to do. This book should set you on the right road, whether you are an electronic technician out to protect your own valuables, or someone who wants to set up and maintain his own protective systems.

Byron G. Wels

Contents

8 COMMERCIAL EQUIPMENT

Build it Yourself Kit—Ready to Operate Equipment—Advanced Devices Laboratory Inc.—ADT: American District Telegraph Co.—Alarmtronics Engineering, Inc.—The Artronix Surveillance System—Ballistics Control Corp.—Bourns Security Systems, Inc.—Concord Electronics—Detex Corporation—Electronic Locator Corp.—Holmes Electric Protective Company—Multi-Elmacs Security System—Pyrotronics, Inc.—Radar Devices Manufacturing Co.—Sylvania's Burglar & Fire Alarm System—Trine Manufacturing Corp.—Summary.

Chapter 1

Personal & Property Security Systems

Check any good foreign intrigue novel, and you'll find at least one character who has his dispatch case handcuffed to his wrist during one episode in the story at least. If the writer's story line was good the courier didn't even have a key to the handcuffs, but the sender and recipient each had duplicate keys! In his effort to protect certain valuables, man has devised some ingenious gadgets that were built into dispatch cases to foil snatchers. One of these, which was very impressive, contained a small triggering mechanism. Once the device was set, the courier had to keep the trigger depressed. If he released it, as would happen when somebody snatched the case, three telescoping legs shot out, each about 12 feet long. The snatcher couldn't get very far, and certainly not very fast.

You've got to remember in setting up such a personal protection system that firearms, especially concealed firearms, are illegal in most big cities, and that even a protective device can be illegal. Tear gas, and more recently mace, have been looked upon as excellent defense devices. But when they are used, the user is subject to imprisonment under some local ordinances. Far more practical are the alarm systems which issue a piercing, high-frequency shriek when triggered. These always attract attention, and the best thing a snatcher can do when he sets one off is to drop the case and run!

Triggering systems for such units are fairly simple. One compact shrieker operates with a closed-circuit jack and a small pin to which a lanyard is attached. When the pin is removed, the jack closes and the siren goes off. The unit can be placed in a pocket and activated simply by pulling the pin. In a ladies hand bag, the lanyard is attached to a ring on her finger, so that separating the bag from the hand triggers the alarm. Other units have more elaborate triggering systems in which a spring-loaded mount supports a steel ball. When the unit is tipped off center, so the ball falls against a metal ring, the alarm sounds.

In making such an installation, start with a small experiment. With the screecher on the work bench, trigger it and listen to the sound level. Now place the screecher inside the bag, purse or case you are planning to protect, and close the unit. You'll see a fantastic decrease in noise level, and in some of the better-quality cases or bags, a decrease so great that the unit is rendered totally ineffective. The point is that the unit which produces the sound must be coupled to free air in order to work at its best. This would mean actually cutting a good-size hole in the case to mount the unit, and then trying to dress over the cut as best you can to avoid any possibility of making the case look any more ugly than necessary.

We have found that with most leather or wood-and-leather cases, or even plastic cases, you can do a fairly respectable job by making the cutout to fit, and then slipping the dress or trim piece of the screecher through from the front. Cement the unit itself into place at the back with either a pliobond cement or one of the more rubbery silastic RTV compounds.

Unfortunately, we don't always think clearly when we're under attack, and personal attack can be a frightening thing. A strong arm suddenly wrapped around your throat, cutting off your breathing, or the flash of a knife blade as it moves toward your middle, can drive any idea of sounding an alarm right out of your mind, and well it should. Sometimes an alarm might cause an attacker to panic, and do you more bodily harm than he had intended.

Mugging is a problem, especially in large urban areas. This author has solved the problem neatly with a huge German Shepherd that is truly menacing. Even people with the very best intentions give her a wide berth as we walk down the street, and we unhesitatingly venture forth in the public parks at any hour of the day or night. When people do approach and ask if she's friendly, we assure them that she is not friendly, and is attack-trained (not true!).

Protecting an individual against attack is not an easy matter, and while self-defense courses are being offered in karate, jui-jitsu and other oriental arts, it is for the electronic technician to devise a means for self defense that requires no effort on the part of the user, yet will prove effective in either apprehending the attacker afterwards or thwarting the attack altogether.

One very effective method that we have seen is simplicity itself. Simply prepare a small piece of absorbent paper towelling as follows: Obtain invisible phosphorescent powder (Edmund Scientific stocks this) and make a saturated solution with light penetrating oil. Soak the paper towelling in the solution, then carefully fold it into a small rectangle, about three inches square. The penetrating oil will remain liquid for a good, long time. Anybody that filches a wallet and a folded paper will feel impelled to open the towelling to see what of value might be contained therein. In so doing, he indelibly marks his fingers with the oil which will easily reveal its presence under black light.

Two other defense devices are certainly worthy of consideration here. One is derived from an old rough-and-tumble fighter's trick. If you're a true gourmet, there's nothing illegal about carrying your own high quality pepper to avoid using the stuff dispensed in restaurants. So form several small tissue-paper packets, each with a quantity of table pepper, and place one in each accessible pocket. When you're assaulted, reach for one of the packets, burst it open with a thumbnail, and toss the entire contents into your assailant's eyes. While he's fighting for his vision, you can calmly decide to either take to your heels, or sail into him. Either way, you're no longer a victim.

The other system is based on the device used to herd tomorrow's steaks aboard freight trains. Electrical cattle prods have two terminals at the end, and a small pushbutton switch. Closing the switch energizes a coil-capacitor system, supplied by a small battery, to provide a high-powered electrical shock at the terminals. If the prod is brought into contact with an assailant, it will rapidly discourage further attempts to attack.

Regarding methods of self-defense, the author suggests that you clip the following out of this book and carry it in your billfold. The next time you're assaulted, pull out the clipping and read it:

I am a black-belt karate expert.

My hands are registered as lethal

weapons with the police department

of this city. I am required by law

to inform you that in any encounter

with me, you may be seriously in-

jured or perhaps killed.

Now you calmly replace the billfold in your pocket, assume a karate-like attack stance, and proceed to get "mobilized."

PERSONAL DEFENSE AND WARNING DEVICES

Like most other alarm systems, the object is to react to "intrusion." The question that arises is just how do you want to react? No doddering little old lady is going to "ki-yi" and stave off a purse snatcher with a forehand chop. And a group of muggers isn't likely to be stopped by a shrieking pocket siren. Many people in urban areas have taken to carrying tear gas pens illegally, in the hope that should they ever be required to use these, the authorities will simply confiscate the weapon and they'll sacrifice only the six bucks they spent.

No, personal defense against attack is a difficult proposition, and even a person who is under attack is sometimes reluctant to administer a defense in which his attacker can be killed or permanently maimed. So you begin with the question. "If you are attacked, just what do you want to happen?" Obviously, you want the attack stopped and for your assailant to leave you in peace. To best accomplish this, you must outpoint the attacker or frighten him off. If he approaches you with a knife, and you pull a gun, you have outpointed him. Frightening him off is a much surer answer.

But to frighten an assailant is a difficult matter, for such an attacker is usually already frightened when he commences the attack. He's prepared for the very worst, and the best thing you can do is to remain calm. Observe him carefully and make as many mental notes as you can that will assist the police in identifying him later on. Then quietly explain that you don't want any trouble, that your credit cards are insured, that you are willing to cooperate and don't want to get hurt.

Chances are that your assailant will take what valuables he can, as quickly as possible, and depart in all haste. He may feel more secure by knocking you to the ground to reduce the possibility of pursuit. It is after he departs that you can take action to have him apprehended. Rest assured that any warning, shrieking sirens during the attack itself will result in harm to you, even if the devices are not under your control.

PROPERTY WARNING SYSTEMS

When man commences to gather valuable possessions about himself, other men, not quite so fortunate, covet those things. It all goes back to the door, a handy contrivance used to keep intruders (including the elements) out of a man's home. Unhappily, the door had to be provided with a means for opening and closing so the owner of the house could get in and out. However, as such ease of entry was available to him, so it was to every man, and the lock was invented. Now (theoretically) only the man with a key could gain entrance.

In rapid succession were invented the lock picks, the skeleton key, and the second-story man who didn't bother with doors and locks but favored upper windows. Wealthy men took to hiring other men whose duty was to protect the wealthy man's property. Before long, municipal guards, called police, came into being.

But as protective science became more sophisticated, so did the methods and techniques of burglars. Some of the devices they employed to offset man's protection are as interesting as the protective devices they managed to defeat. The so-called "slam lock" on a door contains a beveled bar that slides into the lock as the door is closed, then snaps out to bar the door when the door is firmly shut. Once the bar has entered its receptacle in the door jamb, the only way to open the door from the outside is with a properly fitting key. However, if you have a fairly rigid piece of plastic (any credit card will do), simply insert it between the door and the jamb

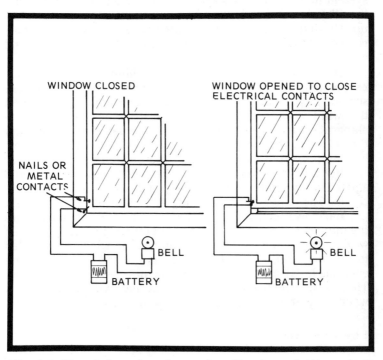

Fig. 1-1. Simple burglar alarm circuit using a battery, bell and two metal contacts (nails).

at the lock level and push. The card will slide against the tapered bar and force it back into the lock, permitting you to easily open the door—without a key!

Man is not to be so easily outwitted, however, and the straight bar became popular, which could not be opened with a plastic card (that process, incidently, is called "loiding" in the underworld, a corruption of "celluloiding" as celluloid was used long before plastics came on the scene.) The straight bar seemed the perfect lock, but burglars found a way to get around that also. Any automobile bumper jack could be placed between the two upright door jambs at the lock level. A few simple pumps of the jack and the jamb is spread sufficiently to allow the burglar to easily push the door open.

With the advent of electricity, the protection picture changed drastically. Suddenly, it was relatively easy to protect a home. With a nail or metal contact driven part-way into a window frame and another into the window support, if the window was opened beyond a certain point the two nails touched and sounded an alarm. The circuit of this basic system in Fig. 1-1 shows one nail connected to a battery and the other to a bell. The bell is wired to the other battery terminal. Had a would-be thief attempted to raise a window rigged with this system, the contacts would have touched and activated the bell.

Doors were easily protected with sliding-actuator switches that closed when a door was opened. Glass storefronts suddenly sprouted metallic-ribbon decorations that framed the window with foil. The foil strips were connected to elaborate alarm systems that triggered when the window (and the foil strip) was broken. Man once again felt secure, for now he was protected by electricity—the ultimate servant.

But burglars had access to the technology as well, and started carrying small clip leads, just like those on your workbench. The first step in breaking and entering was to defeat the alarm system by shorting the terminals of the alarm with the clip lead. Now the decorative metal strip could be broken with impunity and the alarm would remain silent, blindfolded to the intrusion by a simple clip lead. Naturally, the game continued. Electrical intrusion alarms became electronic. They became more difficult to defeat and bypass. And that's when another unwanted intruder was introduced on the scene.

Fire Protection

As long as the premises are wired to trigger an alarm in the event of intrusion, it's a simple matter to add heat sensors and make the system do double duty as a fire alarm. A few handsome plastic buttons are simply placed where fire is most likely to break out and wired into the system. Should the temperature suddenly elevate, the alarm will sound. Unfortunately, smoke is frequently a more dire problem than flame or elevated temperature. Danger from smoke can long precede damage from flame . But, thanks to his seemingly infinite resources, man has devised photoelectric smoke detectors that will trigger an alarm when smoke is present. Smoke detectors, such as the unit shown in Fig. 1-2, which is available in "kit" form, are priced within reach of most homeowners. Used in combination with heat sensors, the home would appear to be totally protected against damage from fire.

Protecting Your Car

If modern man has a home away from home, it certainly must be his automobile. And, just like a home, an automobile

Fig. 1-2. Heathkit smoke detector, Model GD-87. Units such as this are suitable for many protective installations.

is a tempting target for a thief. Certain components are easy to remove and turn over to a middleman (called a "fence") for disposition. The actual thief, the one who breaks and enters, gets small value for his risk and effort, but the fence does quite well, endangered only by a puny punishment for receiving stolen merchandise. The automobile offers the thief a number of "commodities" for quick turnover. Hub caps are easy to remove, come off quickly and easily, and are good for a few cents each. In large urban areas, they are the common target for youngsters. More advanced thieves will strip valuables from a car in no time at all. A jack and a series of four concrete blocks under the axles, and there go your wheels—tires and all. Once the thief gains access to the inside of the car, you can kiss radio, tape player, and heater goodbye. In the trunk and under the hood there's the battery, spare tire, and anything else the thief cares to grab.

More sophisticated thieves jump the ignition switch and drive it to a receiving garage where serial numbers are obliterated and the paint job is re-done. The next thing you know, your car is on its way to South America for sale at a heck of a good profit. Sometimes youngsters take a car for an evening of joy riding, then leave the "borrowed" car in another part of town.

To protect your car, the first thing that may occur to you is to wire an alarm to the refrigerator-like switch in the door jamb that turns on the interior lights when the door is opened. However, of all the commercial alarms we've run across, the most outstanding is sold by General Cement Corporation. It's an electronic sensor that triggers the alarm when a change in battery current drain occurs. If a thief so much as opens the door of the car, causing the dome light to go on, the alarm is triggered. Even the light in the glove compartment will sound the alarm.

Such alarm systems must have a defeat; you don't want the alarm to sound when you get into the car yourself. The usual method is to mount a key-operated switch elsewhere on the car. When you leave the car, you turn a key in the switch and the alarm is set. Open the circuit to defeat the switch when you return. This brings up another point. It is the purpose of an intrusion alarm system to discourage an intrusion. The defeat switch, therefore, should be mounted on the driver's side of the car—easily visible on the side of the fender. It is not only more convenient this way, but any professional thief will recognize it for what it is, and leave the car alone—and that's just what you want.

When you purchase any intrusion alarm system, the manufacturer usually supplies a decal for a nearby window which warns the would-be thief that the property is protected. In fact, more than one clever distributor sells decals only! Put a warning decal on your property, attesting to the fact that the property is electronically-protected, and you may not even need an intrusion alarm system!

Chapter 2

Selling Protection

How do you go about selling the service of protection? The best way to start is to make up your mind to the fact that there is indeed a need for this service in your area—and that the need is not being fulfilled. You may live in Peaceful Valley, where there hasn't been a burglary or a house-breaking in the last umpteen years! But even if that is the case, isn't fire an ever-present hazard? In a situation of that sort, you sell fire protection, with intrusion protection as an added feature.

You then decide what type systems will best suit the area in which you live or work. Obviously, if you live in the remote hinterlands, away from any large urban center, a system of patrols, or one which depends on summoning aid from a central office, is not for you. To help you learn what is available, there is a "catalog" section at the end of this book, which explains the various commercial systems you can purchase.

To get started, invest in an advertisement in your local newspaper. Many manufacturers cooperate in such advertising by offering you free cuts or mats to make the ad more suitable and attractive. The newspaper will insert a post office box number for you, or your name and address. When the ad appears, sit back and wait for the letters to come in.

Another approach is to telephone prospective clients for an appointment at a time when the husband is at home. One chap we know makes a very dramatic entrance to his prospective client's home. He asks the client to please lock all doors and windows so the home is "secure," and announces that he will arrive at 8:00 that evening. At 8:00 arrive he does, either by forcing a window or picking the lock. He always makes a sale. Explain to the client that yours is a highly personal business, and that the system you select with them will be tailored to their requirements. Then you proceed to find out just what their requirements are. By all means, make notes. Go through the home with the family, and offer suggestions as to where protection may be required. Remember that you are the expert and that they are depending on you.

SYSTEM REQUIREMENTS

Start with doors and windows. Intruders ordinarily do not break and enter through walls, if more convenient openings are available. A rough floor plan of the house won't hurt in your evaluation, either. But don't forget cellar doors and windows which can provide access to the house as well. Usually, interior doors do not require protection if the outside of the house is well guarded. However, if the home has (for example) eight cellar windows and one outside cellar door, you might point out that the one interior door that gives access to the cellar can be more economically protected if no valuables are kept in the cellar! In this preliminary evaluation, what you are doing is determining the number and type of detectors that will be required.

As you analyze the system needed, to begin you must also attempt to determine how elaborate a system the resident is considering. One gentleman, whose eldest daughter was on a strict diet, wanted an additional alarm, totally independent of the rest of the system, that would sound if she raided the refrigerator!

Going over the floor plans of the home and the information you've collected, you have to start thinking like a crook. How would you break and enter, if you wanted to? If you did get in, what would you remove? Is the family away from home for a sufficient part of the day so the system is the only protection available? And what about alarm methods and systems? What would best foil a burglar? Do you want an audible alarm to sound to frighten him away? Do you prefer a telephone dialer-repeater to notify the local police so the thief can be nabbed in the act? You must come up with sound recommendations for your client that will be viable, suitable, and within his budgetary limits. You must offer the client a choice of systems, within the same general price structure, and don't forget to include the time and labor of making the installation.

At this point, you have to be a salesman, too. Decide well in advance which system you think is best for him, and why. Be sure you suggest additional ancillary devices (such as heat detectors or smoke detectors) that can be installed almost at cost while the system is going in but that would be quite a bit more costly if you had to make an additional trip to put them in later. Explain the value of compound alarm systems, in which local as well as remote alarms are included. Offer outdoor alarms which will wake neighbors who can phone the police if the resident is not at home. And make sure you specify a defeat, a small key-operated switch, to cut off the alarms

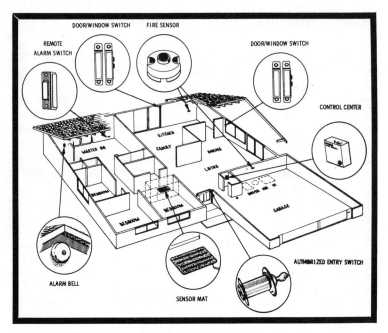

Fig. 2-1. Floor plan of a typical house showing locations of sensors for intrusion and fire protection. (Courtesy Sylvania)

when they are not in use. These lock switches come with at least two keys, one of which should be delivered to the local police precinct with instructions for its use. Offer, too, a "test" switch, with which the resident can at any time ascertain that the system is working.

EVALUATING SYSTEMS

How do you know what's best for a client's needs? You start with a program of self-education. Write to the various firms listed in this book and obtain the information you will need to make such evaluations. While you are writing, ask if they will sell you the basic equipment and recommend the proper markup costs. You're certain to come out with the information you need.

But you've got to know before you start exactly what's available. Remember that your client is depending on you—as the expert—to tell him what he needs. For example, a residential dwelling in which people or pets may move freely about the home during the night is scarcely the place for a sonic system that can be triggered by ordinary movement! Yet such a system would be ideal for protecting a place of business where there should be no movement whatever after the business day is over.

Remember, too, that your client called because he's frightened. While you represent an outlay of money, it's money he will deem well spent if it does the job. So when you make a suggestion, be ready to stand behind it and justify it, and be ready, too, to answer the question "why?" It will be asked often, almost as often as "how much?"

Watch out for that word "guarantee." It's an easy one to use and it is rife with hidden meanings that can backfire legally. You can certainly guarantee to make an installation in accordance with the plans to which you and the client have mutually agreed. You can guarantee to install certain equipment in a workmanlike manner. You can guarantee to appear on a regular and routine basis to check the equipment and to be sure it is in suitable working order. But do **not** guarantee the equipment itself—the manufacturer does that. And above all, do **not** guarantee that the house will never be burglarized, for a careless home owner can forget to turn the system on for the night, and there you are with egg on your face.

Prepare a proposal in a business-like manner, written document which states exactly what work you will do and specifies what equipment will be installed. It sets forth the price, and serves as a reminder specifically what is to be done and what has been done. It should also specify the date on which the work is to be completed. It is prepared in duplicate, one for him, one for you. When you and your client agree on terms, you're ready to go to work.

Obviously, you will have to wire the home, install lock switches, install detectors, and in general, upset the customer's routine for awhile. You're going to be drilling, sawing, and nailing. This is all well and good, but if you want some of the best free advertising available—"word-of-mouth," then work quickly, politely, neatly and carefully. If you will need a step ladder, bring one with you. Don't use the family's prized Louis Quatorze chair. If you drill a hole in the door jamb for the switch lock, spread some paper to catch the shavings first and clean up afterwards. Bring whatever tools and equipment you need to complete the job.

INSTALLATION WORK

Usually, installation instructions will come with the system you select, but there are certain rules to follow.

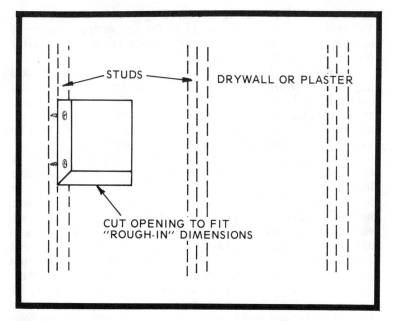

STUDS

DRYWALL OR PLASTER

CUT OPENING TO FIT "ROUGH-IN" DIMENSIONS

Fig. 2-2. Flush-mount master control panels can be used with dry wall or plaster walls. The "roughing-in" box is screwed to a wall stud.

Generally, you'll find that your clients feel a job is more professional if it is "built-in," rather than just a series of components that are wired together.

When it comes to "building-in," the biggest problem is usually the master control box, but this can be reduced to relatively simple terms with a bit of forethought. Most manufacturers supply their units with either a finished cabinet, designed to place on a shelf, or with a "roughing-in" box, which consists of a hollow surround, open at both ends. Make sure that the wall in which you intend to make the installation is sufficiently thick to contain the unit, and then determine the wall's construction.

The drywall, sheetrock or plasterboard wall will present little or no problem. Locate a vertical stud and cut into the plasterboard on one side of the wall with a keyhole or saber saw. Carefully enlarge the hole (use a template if one is provided), then install the roughing-in box by attaching it with screws to the nearby stud (Fig. 2-2). You will find that the trim panel will cover the saw work, making such an installation simple and neat. If the wall is plaster over lath, the work is admittedly a bit-more difficult, for a cold chisel may be required. However, the technique is essentially the same. You may find a heavy pair of wire cutters handy, if wire lath was used under the plaster. The plaster may require a bit of touchup spackling after the roughing-in box is installed. This should be done immediately so it will dry before the balance of the unit is installed.

WIRING

The object of the installation is to make it as inconspicuous as possible. This means that wiring from point to point must be equally unobtrusive. Examine the room. Are there mouldings or trim pieces that you can take advantage of for purposes of concealment? If not, you will find at least one manufacturer who can provide you with wiring that is flat, with a sticky surface that needs only to be pressed into place. Wiring is also available with a variety of colored insulations that you nearly lose sight of when placed against a matching background! Where nothing else will do, you will have to use an assortment of clips made of plastic that will hold the wiring in position, just the way you want it. Where all else fails, there's always the U-shaped staple.

When you have completed the wiring installation, you will want to test the system. If a local alarm is to be used only, start by pressing the "test" button. The alarm should sound. Now, go from station to station, testing each detector, and make sure that each is functioning. Have somebody stand at the master switch with the key in the lock. This is particularly important for the fire warning devices, for you test these by holding a match or cigarette lighter under the detector until it goes off. To stop the alarm, the switch must be turned off until the unit cools down and returns to normal. If a remote (outside) alarm is installed, test it briefly and then disconnect one of the wires leading to it so the constant sounding during the subsequent tests will not disturb or alarm neighbors.

With the entire system installed and functioning, explain its operation to the client, and give him the keys. Provide him with all guarantees that came with the equipment, in case of failure, and a card bearing your name, address and telephone number, should he require any additional assistance. Then tell him to make it a point to notify his neighbors that he has installed the alarm system, and that if they hear the alarm go off, to please notify the police at once. You'd be surprised at how much additional business this will bring in for you, too!

Also, advise the client that he should have only as many duplicate keys made as there are members of his immediate household who have house keys. He should show each member how to use the system—turn it on and off—and when. One key should be left with the local police, along with a house key, and full instructions.

And consider future business, too. The man who has you install a system in his home is you greatest ally, for if you've done a good, proper, and reasonable job, chances are that you'll be hearing from his friends, neighbors and family as well. Of course, this man is still a potential customer, for chances are that you can easily sell him an additional system for his car, and perhaps his place of business!

SERVICE

Probably, the important thing here is that you are selling a service, and it's a continuing service, too. You'll be showing up periodically to test the system and make sure everything is still in good working order. Make each such call a sales call, too! Be prepared to show the newest and latest in available devices. For example, the customer who bought the barest minimum three months ago, and rejected completely the idea of a dialer-caller at the time, might now be ready to consider such an addition. And that's another sale for you. And the sales pitch you made for fire protection in addition to intrusion might have been turned down originally, but now the client has been thinking about it and ready to go.

But remember your limitations, and don't over-extend yourself. Rest assured that your customer isn't going to simply allow the system to be installed and then forget about it. He's going to be showing it off to guests, and when he does, he'll be testing it each time. If it should fail, as what electronic component can't, you're going to get a hurry-up call. And your indignant client is going to ask "What if that had been a crook, or a fire?" And you'll have to answer for the system.

And that's where the "service" part of the business comes in. We can assume that you've done a fantastically good installation job, with no loose connections and no shorts or opens. And that the trouble is in the equipment the manufacturer sent. By substitution, you can show the client that the installation was not at fault, and then return the defective component to the manufacturer for repair or replacement. Should the unit be out of warranty, you can either attempt a repair yourself or you can return it to the manufacturer for a complete going-over at a moderate price, then re-sell it later on.

Chapter 3

Rolling Your Own

Technicians or those who like to "build things" may have already devised a super-duper burglar stopper. The electronic magazines have been presenting great and inexpensive ideas for systems that you can build or modify, and quite frankly, save a big chunk of dough over having to buy ready-mades from the manufacturers.

What's the real story behind this practice? If you can, should you? What are the hidden traps and pitfalls? For one thing, you've got to stand behind the products you sell. There aren't any manufacturers backing you up with guarantees (that word again!) and if problems come up, you may find that you carry more responsibility than you might have cared to.

Let's take an extreme case: You construct a foolproof intrusion alarm system, and it goes awry. I know we said "foolproof," but unforeseen things can occur. Let's go a step further and say that the homeowner who buys your system is not insured, that a fire breaks out, the system is defeated, and perhaps even blamed as a cause. Can you see the possible implications?

On the other hand, there is the temptation of greater profits and the possibility of a manufacturing business as well. After all, even the biggest names in the business had to start with a product and run the same risks. . . Why not take the remote chance and build something truly solid? Of course you can. And if this is the route you ultimately elect to follow, make sure of your product first. Be sure that it offers a unique and necessary adjunct that is totally unavailable (at the given price) at the present time.

Having come up with such a remarkable idea, you should attempt to take it to market. But as many inventors have found in the past, it isn't all that easy. First let's consider a few possible sources for such ideas. As we said, the regular monthly magazines print plenty of them. And you can, legally, build any one of these for your own use. You can even volunteer to make one for a friend. But when it comes to making them in quantities for sale, you had better check around a little first. The magazine and its contents are protected by copyright. This means that if you make any attempt to duplicate a magazine project for sale, the publisher (and possibly the author of the article) can slap a law suit against you. The general rule is that you must "appreciably change" the circuit before it can be "stolen." You can take a hint of an idea from this book, you can "borrow" a smidgen from another, and come up with something entirely different, new, and "patentable."

PATENTS

Ask any inventor about patents, and he'll give you his own worst experience with the process. First, let's look at how a patent protects (?) the inventor—if at all. To do this, we'll go backwards, by assuming that you have managed to secure a patent (more on that later) and you feel that your idea is securely yours.

Patents are published, and should yours strike the fancy of a manufacturer, he can do one of two things. He can negotiate with you for the exclusive rights to manufacture and market your patent, or he can "appreciably change" it and cut you entirely out of the picture. As we all know, the latter course is far more economical for him, as it is easy to change electronic circuitry and come out with the same result. You used a Colpitts oscillator; he'll use a Hartley. You used a Class B amplifier; he'll make it a Class A. You selected a 47K resistor; he'll get essentially the same results with a 51K. So for us electronic-type inventors, the patent serves more as a means of giving away our ideas than protecting them.

Getting the patent in the first place is an expensive nuisance. You can't do it at all without the help of a specialist called a "patent attorney," and these guys don't work for beans. You describe your idea to him and he puts it into a patent application form, in legal jargonese. You may have the best electronic draftsman in the world do your schematics for you, but it must be done in the patent office style, so you have to pay a legal draftsman to make the drawings for the application. (This writer tried to go the route once and was miffed to find that the patent draftsman made a sketch of the cabinet in which the invention was housed—and omitted the critical schematic!) Now a search of the patent office files in Washington has to be instituted (more expense) to be sure that there are no similar items already protected. Clear? The patent application then goes to a referee who decides if the idea can be made to work. If he contests the idea (and he will) an expert (more cost) will be called in and you still don't know.

No, there's a better way, and if you come up with a protective (or any other) system that you want protected, do what this author does: There's one form of protection against which even a patent can't stand, and that's called "proof of prior published art." When I come up with a new idea, one that is interesting and that I want to protect and promote, I offer it in the form of a magazine article to one of the many publications in the field. It gets published with my name, my schematics, my photographs. The magazine in which it is published is then copyrighted, and I get paid by the magazine for having written the article. The magazine is then circulated, and potential manufacturers see and become interested in the item. However, before they can go into production on my idea, they must gain written permission from the magazine and (even though I sold the story to the publisher) the author as well. The magazine will generally sell the rights to the story back to me for as little as $1.00 and I can negotiate.

I don't know if all this is strictly legal, and you should consult an attorney before going whole hog. But so far, the system has worked well for me, and I've tried every route. If you still feel the need for patent protection, be prepared to invest an additional $2,000 or more before that patent is issued.

MANUFACTURING

Having gotten through the legalistic maze of protection, you are now ready to manufacture, on a small scale. Probably, you will do this on a single basis, to start with, to produce pilot models and get them distributed. But you will surely discover the economics of mass production, and before long will consider the feasibility of silk screening or photo reproducing your circuit boards or other components. You may even find it less costly to buy these boards from another source, just as you purchase your components. Should the idea become a workable one, you will also find that your own time is better spent in sales or managerial duties, rather than in soldering components to the boards. Hey! Now you're an executive, and you have a staff working for you. Obviously, you will test each component, test the unit, and then package it for its own protection.

Another out is to go to a manufacturer who has all the facilities for producing your unit and, by running in your components and parts at the start of his line, can manufacture for you at a reasonable cost and save you all of the headache.

SELLING THE UNIT

Now that you have the manufacturing under control and have the unit protected, you can set up a sales organization. Obviously, the larger your potential sales area, the more sales you can make—and the more money as well. No matter how good a salesman you are, however, there's just so much territory that you can cover alone. You're going to need a national sales force. You will want to establish a distribution system, with outlets all over the country.

Once again, happily, there are such distributors who are tooled up to provide a total and complete sales force for you. However, they make their money by marking up the price, so you had better establish a selling price with sufficient leeway to cover discounting to jobbers, distributors, wholesalers and salesmen, all of whom will want their piece of the commission. Naturally, you want a profit for yourself, and you do have to cover the cost of manufacturing and advertising, don't you? Probably, that system you were planning to sell for a reasonable price is now structured out of sight.

I think there are several points here that require deep and complete consideration. First of all, do not act rashly and go blundering into business in the manner of a bull in a china shop. You can get yourself pretty deeply scarred, and wind up losing more than your business. Business matters are not for amateurs, and you had better obtain (and listen to) some calm, thoroughly experienced businessmen before you go charging forward.

Discouraging? Not by any means! If you are bent on proceeding, by all means, do. All I suggest here is that you know what you are getting into and that you arm yourself with sufficient facts before you go ahead. The chances are that you don't plan a national sales and advertising program, that you simply want to look into the possibility of setting up a small, local business to manufacture and sell, install and service intrusion and fire alarm systems. You certainly can.

SOURCES OF SUPPLY

No customer is going to be intrigued by the idea of un-finished, dangling, rough-looking components. He wants a professional installation that will look as well as the home he is trying to protect and which he obviously thinks enough of to want to protect. If you choose to manufacture your own equipment, do consider the value of a nice looking metal cabinet with controls clearly marked with paint-filled engraving, or at the very least, attractive decals or press-type.

While an exposed thermal contact may work every bit as well as a fancy plastic button for fire protection, the fire protection that is offered by the professional looking plastic button will have more sales appeal. If you have a smoke detector, certainly a one inch hole for the smoke to enter is sufficient from the technical point of view, but a one inch hole that is fitted with a perforated or screened snap hole plug is better.

Talking about that one inch hole, you might make such a hole with a drill and file, or a nibbler, for your own use, or for experiments of a breadboard nature. But for the customer, invest in a chassis punch; make it a nice, smooth, round hole.

You'll find suitable commercially manufactured components in most electronic supply house catalogs, and you should stock sufficient numbers if you decide to go into business, so that your customers aren't kept waiting while you wait for parts. Remember that you sold the customer on the system, and he wants it installed before breakfast yesterday. Your feeble excuses that "the stuff didn't come in yet" are just that—feeble excuses—and will leave you in the unfortunate position of either violating your agreement so the customer can back out, or worse yet, allowing a competitor to steal the sale after you did all the groundwork!

The appeal of manufacturing your own components is undeniable, since your greatest cost in installing intrusion and fire alarm systems will be the systems themselves. So, if you can make that much additional income from each sale, by all means, do so. But remember: If you make your own, you are solely responsible for its performance. You will have to state, in your written agreement with the client, that you will repair or replace the unit at no charge (or for a small service charge) if it fails to function. With the commercially available units, this is taken care of by the manufacturer's guarantee or warranty.

Unfortunately, should the unit fail to function during an actual intrusion, the homeowner can institute proceedings against you, and while the outcome of such litigation is debatable, it would certainly be a lot nicer to have the resources of another manufacturer to fall back on in a case of this sort.

Chapter 4

Service & Maintenance

According to Murphy's Law, if anything can go wrong, it will! This applies to intrusion and fire alarm systems as well as most other electronic devices. However, what goes wrong and when it goes wrong is highly critical, as far as you are concerned. Don't allow anything to go wrong at a critical time. Should the system decide to fail during a break or when fire breaks out, somebody's sure as heck going to look cross-eyed at you. The same applies to what goes wrong. A failure at a crucial time is bad enough, but if the failure comes as a result of a shabby job of installation, you're going to have a lot of explaining to do.

TWO KINDS OF SERVICE

There are two types of servicing with which you will be involved: routine preventive maintenance, and occasional corrective maintenance. If you set up a system test circuit with the installation, it's a simple matter for the homeowner to periodically test the system's efficacy himself by simply pressing a test button. He presses the button once in awhile, hears the alarm sound, and he's happy. If the system includes a remote alarm or a police or fire call, he periodically calls the correct agency to notify them of the test, makes the test, then calls back to confirm that they received the call and that the test is completed. However, you should arrange for periodic calls, perhaps on a monthly basis, to test each component of the system.

During these periodic tests, you should check each detector to see that it is functioning properly. Smoke detectors can easily be tested with an ordinary cigar. Heat detectors can be checked with a match held under the detector button. For a more accurate test, set a soldering iron and thermostat to the heat specified for the particular button and apply the iron to the button.

Intrusion circuits should be checked by actually operating them. With the master key switch closed and operable, open the door; open the windows. Test each element of the circuit independently and individually. Make sure that all alarm systems operate and function.

IN CASE OF FAILURE

Should any element fail, two things must be done immediately. The element should be replaced at once and the faulty element analyzed to determine the reason for failure. To determine whether or not a detector is defective, simply jump its contacts with a clip lead. If the alarm sounds, the detector failed to respond to the proper stimulus and should be removed.

Assuming that you have done a serviceable job of installation, and that prime quality components have been used unstintingly, the part of the system most apt to fail will be the "little black box" or the electronic circuitry. If it was commercially produced, the warranty or guarantee should be examined. If it is still under the manufacturer's coverage, the unit should be returned to him at once for repair. If the unit is not so protected, you may attempt a repair yourself. Under no circumstances should you attempt such a repair while the unit is still under warranty; in most cases, such tampering voids the warranty and will cost your client even more dearly, should you have to return the unit after your own repair efforts have failed. During the time that the unit is out, the home or premises are left unprotected. If at all possible (for such repairs can often take weeks), provide a substitute unit until the repaired system is returned.

FAIL-SAFE

Most units incorporate a fail-safe system which should be routinely tested. In most fail-safes, the normal power supply holds a relay or latching circuit closed. Should primary power fail, however, the relay releases and a battery-operated alarm notifies the homeowner that power to the system has failed. As batteries have only a limited shelf life, some means must be provided to monitor or check the fail-safe circuit if one is employed.

Banks are particularly susceptible to intrusion, and they are highly conscious of it. As a result, any new and sufficiently appealing device is difficult not to sell to a bank—and not instead of but in addition to the equipment currently extant. In banks and stores, you'll find hidden television cameras and constant photo-surveillance devices. As you can appreciate, these take a knowledge of the field of photography. Unless you

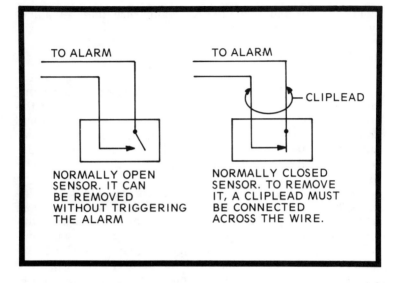

Fig. 4-1. One of these two basic type sensors are used in an alarm.

are particularly well versed in these areas, do not undertake to service them.

JUMPING DETECTORS

When a detector malfunctions, first determine its type. If it opens a circuit when it is triggered (normally closed type), an ordinary clip lead can be used to jump the circuit, after which the detector can easily be removed without triggering the alarm, as shown in Fig. 4-1. If the detector is of the type that closes a circuit when triggered (normally open type), it can be removed without a jumper wire for servicing. When any detector mechanism (fire or intrusion) is removed for servicing, it should be replaced at once. When a detector fails the replacement element should be on hand and installed before you leave the premises. Remember that simply because the alarm does not trigger does not mean that the premises are protected! And the owner is paying you for protection—not the installation of a system.

Where a continuous foil ribbon is used to protect glass, you will occasionally find that normal occupancy of the premises can damage the foil strip. Carrying bulky items in or out through such a protected glass door can often result in a cut or scratch through the foil, and this can result in damage to the strip's continuity. Since the strip is generally covered with lacquer, and since available cements are rarely conductive, we searched for and found a means to repair such breaks without having to restrip the entire surface.

With light sandpaper or emery cloth, sand the strip above and below the cut or tear, so all of the lacquer is removed. Check with an ohmmeter to be sure that the lacquer is removed on both sides of the break. Using a razor blade, remove the strip so at least a quarter of an inch of glass shows on both sides of the break. Make sure the glass surface is clean; wipe it with trichlorethylene or carbon tetrachloride.

Using liquid silver print, the type used for repairing printed-circuit boards, paint the area of clear glass, making sure the silver print overlaps the tape at both sides of the break. Allow it to dry thoroughly, then test for total continuity at the strip's terminals. If a high-resistant continuity is present, this means that either insufficient lacquer has been removed, or that the silver print paint has not been applied heavily enough. Try another coat before resanding. When satisfied that continuity is present, the rough edges of the paint can be removed with the razor blade, and the whole area can then be relacquered.

You (and your clients) must realize that a home-protection system is not like a television set. A unit that has been sold by you to the client will be called to your attention when a failure takes place. It is then for you to decide whether to effect a repair or return the unit to the manufacturer for such repairs. As the seller, you should find out from the manufacturer just how far you can go with repairs before endangering the unit's warranty or guarantee. To avoid what the manufacturer would call "tampering," a paper seal is often placed over a nut or screw that must be removed to gain access to the innards of the unit. Where paper seals aren't used, a drop of paint or lacquer usually is. Any attempt to open the box will break such a seal, and usually void the warranty.

It rather reminds me of Al, a radio repairman in the '30s. One day a neighbor brought in a standard 5-tube superhet, saying it worked until five minutes ago, and then quit. Al opened the back of the unit and started pulling the tubes to find the bad one. The first one he yanked was a 35Z5 rectifier. So was the second—and the third. . . The set had five 35Z5s! There wasn't a grid in the whole set!

"You sure this set was working?"
"Uh-huh."

"**You** didn't try to fix it, did you?"

"Uh-uh. I know you guys charge more if a customer tries to fix the set himself."

I guess that's true. Al sold the customer four more tubes at list price.

SERVICING SPECIALIZED EQUIPMENT

The more possessions a man surrounds himself with, the more specialized will be the equipment that he uses to protect these possessions. And man hasn't just recently decided that his valuables were worth protecting. In many urban areas, it used to be commonplace to carry a small mousetrap in your pocket to foil would-be pickpockets! Today, we have wallets that will sound an alarm when a pocket is picked. We have alarms that will sound when a car is stolen. Let's get into that for a moment.

I live in Manhattan, which is a part of New York City. I wouldn't own a car here, for it just doesn't pay. The taxes are foolishly high and are going up, insurance rates are prohibitive, and parking—ah! The parking!

In New York City, our regular garbage removals are facilitated by a process called "alternate side" parking. You can park on one side of the street on Mondays, Wednesdays and Fridays, on the other side on Tuesdays, Thursdays and Saturdays. With so many cars to be parked, and so little space (garages rent for almost as much as homes do), a car owner must often park his car many, many blocks from where he lives. The process involves driving up one street and down another until you do find a place to park, and sometimes you wind up so far away that you have to take a cab home!

Well, one night some super-careful citizen parked under my bedroom window, locked his car, and turned on the built-in intrusion alarm system. It was pretty late at night that someone tried to break into the car. The horn started to sound: "BEEP BEEP BEEP BEEP BEEP BEEP BEEP BEEP..."

The police promised to be right there. They weren't right there. The darned horn kept right on going, and then mercy of mercies, the battery began to give out. The beeping got fainter and fainter, "beep beep beep beep beep beep..." Then it stopped altogether—for two hours, until the battery got its second wind, and it started again.

There have been other attempts to protect, with home-brewed and special equipment, that have backfired too many times to be worthwhile. One chap wired a spark coil to the frame of his car, so that anyone who touched the car would get an electric shock. Effective? Yes, so effective that the owner of the car landed in jail. You are **not** allowed to create a public hazard, and the decision of the judge was that everybody that touches a car parked on a public thoroughfare is not doing so with malice aforethought!

In another much publicized case, a farmer rigged a loaded shotgun at a doorway to blast any intruders. An intruder broke and entered, and the gun went off, seriously injuring the would-be thief. He was not killed, and on recovery from his wounds, sued the farmer in court, openly admitting that he intended to break and enter the premises with robbery as his motive. He won the case, too. There's always a strong temptation to incorporate a firearm or tear-gas device or some other pain-inflicting element into a system designed to protect a given premises from intrusion. These should either be assiduously avoided, or should be thoroughly investigated for all possible ramifications beforehand.

People can get pretty upset when their homes have been invaded by an intruder, and after the initial shock wears off, they determine that this shall never happen again. They will spare nothing in the protection of their homes, and want only the very worst to befall the intruder. They want him to suffer for even daring to think of such an attempt again. But such over-reaction must be discouraged and wisdom made to prevail. The owner of the premises must be content with having the intruder either frightened off or apprehended for police action. He must never take the law into his own hands. Such action can have dire consequences, and if you provide such a system for him, you'll be amazed at how quickly, in a court of law, you become an accessory to the fact.

PRINCIPLES OF ALARM SYSTEMS

The most usual alarm is designed to give warning that a break (or make) in the circuit protecting the premises has taken place. There are three basic types of alarms, which can be used individually or in combination. The first is a loud alarm designed to waken the residents or their neighbors and alert them to the fact of intrusion or fire. Such alarms are also designed to alert an intruder to the fact that his presence has been detected. This sort of system is designed to frighten the intruder into a rapid departure. In most cases, this will suffice. For the intruder is generally very much in tension when he enters somebody else's home illegally. He only wants to secure what valuables he can and depart safely. But, sometimes an intruder who is under the influence of drugs or alchohol is not thinking rationally, and may elect to stand and

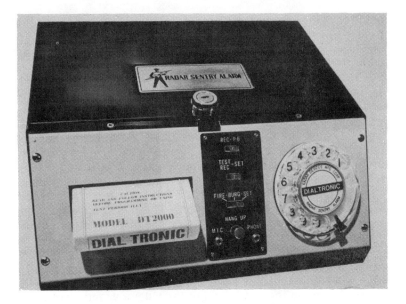

Fig. 4-2. Dialtronic Model DT-2000 designed to alert police or a central agency of an intrusion or fire.

fight. You should also know that most states make a distinction between "robbery" and "armed robbery," with the latter carrying a far heavier sentence. Professional burglars assiduously avoid the possession of firearms.

The second type of alarm is a local alarm, designed to alert a resident to the fact that his premises have been entered but not to sound an alert to the intruder. This enables the homeowner to either telephone the proper authorities, or to grab a poker or his number five iron and investigate himself. The latter course is, naturally, to be discouraged.

The third basic type of alarm system (Fig. 4-2) is one that automatically dials the telephone to call the local police precinct, and when the phone is lifted at the other end, a prerecorded message says:

"This is a recording. The premises at (address) have been entered by a burglar triggering this alarm. Please send help immediately, as the burglar has not been warned by the alarm system and the intruder is on the premises now."

This type of system has its failings, of course. There is every chance that the duty officer can pick up the phone and say, "One moment, please," and put your call on hold while the message is being transmitted. He comes back to the line and hears nothing! You get around this by making the recording a constant loop, so the message is repeated again and again.

There are, of course, countless variations of these devices, as you shall see. Regardless of the type system, it should be checked periodically. But before initiating a test, be sure to alert those involved—including police or a central agency on dial or other systems designed to alert those agencies—that a test will occur. After the test, confirm that the test was received and that it is completed. In the event of a failure, the faulty unit should be removed for servicing and replaced. Where service is to be an overnight matter, a "loaner" should be installed and checked so the premises are not unprotected while the unit is undergoing repair.

Servicing the first two types of systems is relatively simple—a periodic cleanup, lubrication (where called for),

Fig. 4-3. Shown above is a typical ADT central station, nerve center for electric protection systems installed in subscribers' properties to safeguard against fire, burglary, holdup and other hazards. Upon operation of the protective system within the subscriber's property, or when trouble develops, distinctive signals are automatically transmitted to the central station. On duty around the clock, ADT personnel immediately initiate appropriate action.

reinstallation, and test. In the case of the taped telephone dialer, servicing becomes more complex. The unit should be placed on the bench, and where batteries are used, they should be checked under load for full voltage output. Moving parts should be lubricated with the proper (check with the manufacturer) grade of lubricant where it is called for. Oilite or permanently lubricated parts should receive no oil at all. Plastic and rubber components should not be oiled or lubricated. Dust, dirt and grime should be removed. Tape heads should be demagnetized (after removing the tape cartridge to avoid accidental erasure) and cleaned thoroughly.

This device is basically electromechanical in nature, and can be maintained much in the way that a tape recorder or mechanical device is serviced. Check active voltages according to the manufacturer's service notes, and where a fault in a component part occurs, it should be replaced.

Nothing sells intrusion alarms better than word of mouth, so if you go into the business of selling, make sure that you provide only the best available service to go with the products. You will usually find the many manufacturers happy to cooperate with you.

Chapter 5

Detectors

What is it that you want to detect? That's the way it begins. You will find a very wide assortment of commercially available detecting devices that will activate your control unit, but you have to know first exactly what it is that you want to detect.

If the premises are to be open to a great many people whom you will permit to enter and closed to those you do not want there, the best sort of answer might be an armed guard—a human being with a pair of eyes who will recognize a "pass" issued to those who may enter. Most needs, however, are far less sophisticated.

Cost becomes more than a passing factor, also. A complex radar system that will detect movement in a room might be impressive as all get-out, and cost an arm and half a leg, too! It may break down because of its very complexity, and while it could be the thing for protecting an office that closes at a given hour, it could be inconvenient in a home where family members are free to rove about the house at will. Chances are that a simple photoelectric system, with mirrors used to reflect beams of light back and forth across the room, from source to cell, would be far more practical.

One chap we know rented an office in the city, and shortly thereafter it was burglarized. He lost a couple of small office machines and his petty-cash box. He had a burglar alarm installed, and as he left the office that evening, he turned on the system. He started for home, feeling happy, safe, and secure. As he reached home, his wife was waiting out front to meet him.

"It's the office" she said. "Your alarm went off and they want you downtown immediately."

With his supper cooling on the table, our friend raced back to his office again. He pushed through the crowd around his office door and turned off the alarm.

What triggered the system? The cleaning lady, who cleaned all the offices at night, had used her master key to open his door. He apologized, turned the alarm off, and never

1102

Fig. 5-1. Heat sensor available in open or closed circuit models designed to operate at 135 or 190 degrees. (Courtesy Electronic Locator Div., On-Guard Corp.)

turned it on again. You see, you've got to think of all the possible contingencies!

The detector is a 2-state affair. It's either open or closed. When the intruding element changes the state, the detector triggers the alarm, which will sound. Unfortunately, technicians, in their zeal to develop that which is new, different or unusual, frequently come up with an elaborate (and often unusual) electronic application that can best be served by a far less complex system commonly available from the supply houses. Let's start with fire detectors.

FIRE DETECTORS

These fall into two main types, each of which performs yeoman service for its specific requirements, and each of which has a place in the overall scheme of things. The first is a heat detector, of which there are two basic types: A thermocouple senses changes in heat levels and changes in electrical resistance with such changes. This type of detector operates a control circuit that can trigger a preset alarm when such a change occurs. The advantage is that it can be set to monitor a range of temperatures, so that temperature drop as well as temperature rise can be used to trigger the alarm.

Let's speak frankly for a moment, as we are, in the final analysis, talking about the protection of somebody's investment. With food prices going out of sight these days, many people have taken to purchasing food freezers and stocking them with provisions bought in large quantities to effect money-saving economics. Should a freezer fail, the food within would spoil. A thermocouple alarm system would inform him if such an occurrence were to take place, and he could then make provision to salvage his edibles, perhaps by storing them temporarily with a neighbor while his freezer is being repaired. Without such an alarm, and as most such freezers are placed in basements or garages, he may not know of such a failure until he makes his next trip to the freezer for provisions (or his kids take a look to check on last winter's snowballs!).

Increased temperature, on the other hand, can prove equally critical, for temperatures must often be critically controlled in children's rooms or in sick rooms. But, in general, you will be concerned with elevation in temperature only, and the small thermostatic buttons (Fig. 5-1) are best suited for this. Heat sensor buttons consist of a bi-metallic disc that is flexed and set in plastic so no contact is made with the contact pin beneath it. When the ambient temperature reaches a critical level (determined by and marked on each button), the disc "pops" to make contact with the pin and the circuit closes. These buttons are mounted in nice looking plastic cases with convenience holes for screws and recesses to permit in and out wiring. They are available in different temperature ranges, depending on where you want them placed. Usually, they are spotted where there is the most chance of fire breaking out, or where the most protection is required. Since heat rises, it is generally advisable to place these on the ceiling, above such places as ranges, boilers, etc.

Fig. 5-2. Photoelectric fire (smoke) detector used in Pyrotronics systems. Such sensors are available in a variety of enclosure styles.

The other type of fire detector requires some understanding of how fire and fire damage can occur. A smouldering fire can produce more smoke than flame or heat, and your home can be filled with dense smoke before a heat-sensitive button is activated. This smoke can cause damage and can be hazardous to someone trapped in a smoke-filled room. A smoke detector is a simple photoelectric device that senses a change in the available light to the photocell (Fig. 5-2). When such a change occurs, due to the presence of smoke, the photoelectric cell triggers the alarm mechanism through the control circuit.

The general procedure, usually, is to spot a few heat-sensing buttons throughout the house and place only one smoke detector at a centrally critical point in the house. The author disagrees with this procedure, and strongly recommends that the heat sensors be placed wherever there is a danger of elevated temperature and that more than one smoke detector be used wherever there is danger from smoke.

Happily, the best smoke detector is your nose. You can usually smell smoke before it gets heavy enough to do severe damage. And yes, it will waken you, should you be asleep. But there should be at least one such detector wherever there is an open area in the home. Closed-off areas should have their own also.

WATER DETECTORS

What? Yes, that's right. Remember that you are wiring a sensing system, and by adding water detectors, you can offer a measure of protection that people just usually don't think about.

Got a wading pond out back for the kiddies? A water detector placed near the top can be made to sound an alarm if somebody gets into the pool (and raises the water level) when they aren't supposed to. Got a swimming pool? A water detector strategically placed will prevent you from accidently overfilling it. Got a basement that's prone to flooding periodically? A water detector placed on the basement wall will warn you of the rising tide!

While the author was editor of a major electronics magazine, we published a story on a form of water detector that senses the first few raindrops falling through an open window. The detector relays this information to a complex circuit which activates a small motor that closes the window. When the window is fully closed, it triggers a limit switch, which cuts off the entire mechanism. Nice? We thought so.

And you could build this system for less than thirty dollars at that time. With it, you can leave your windows open, and if it begins to rain while you're out, they will automatically close!

We got a letter from a youngster who saw the story in print. He accomplished the same thing more easily. His "detector" consists of a spring-type clothespin with a metal thumb tack in each end. With the pin closed, the tacks make contact, closing the circuit which triggers the motor. To keep the pin open and the tacks apart, he uses a simple aspirin tablet. If you see any television at all, you **know** how fast those things melt!

This home-brewed aspirin detector isn't a half-bad way to sense the presence of unwanted water, and it is far less expensive than some of the high-falutin' electronic gadgets that can sense to a decimal point, a change in the "hum-a-ditty!"

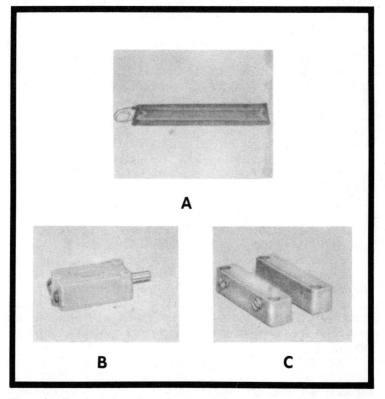

Fig. 5-3. Basic intrusion sensors: step-on mat (A), tamper switch (B), and door or window switches (C). (Courtesy Ballistics Control Corp.)

INTRUSION DETECTORS

In spite of what you may think, intrusion detectors need not be very complicated at all. Consider, if you will, that when you drive over the air hose at your favorite gasoline emporium, a bell rings, telling the operator that you are there. That's an intrusion detector.

A simple rubber mat with a switch in it (Fig. 5-3), placed inconspicuously under the mat in your entry hall, can serve as a fine intrusion detector. And, if you care to stretch the point, the switch that turns on your refrigerator light is, in a sense, an intrusion detector also.

The point is, actually, that anything which serves to operate when an intrusion takes place can be used to operate a control circuit which, in turn, can operate an alarm, telling you that an intrusion has occurred. The simpler the better is generally the rule, and you should consider this when you're evaluating your detector requirements. The more simple you can make the detector, the more elemental and basic, the less there is that can go wrong with it and the more efficiently it will work.

For example, if you want to detect the opening of a window, what could be simpler than a small leaf-actuated switch embedded in the window frame, so that as the window is raised, the switch activates? Why not a similar switch in the jamb of a door, so that opening the door activates the switch? A basic latching relay circuit can be used along with such a system so that once the system is triggered, the alarm will sound until a reset button is pressed. Let's face it: The complex, ornate alarm systems may be necessities for large business firms, but frankly, this writer doubts their value to the average homeowner or apartment dweller.

It comes down to a decision between convenience, cost, and protection. The ever-alert radar system that triggers on movement in a room will be a novelty at first and a nuisance later. The homeowner that goes this route will soon realize that he has more than adequate protection, in fact more than he needs—or wants! And the first few times that a family member or a pet triggers the alarm system, he'll either decide to defeat the system, or his neighbors will talk him into defeating it!

How much is it worth to protect what you own? You can spend several thousand dollars on intrusion alarm systems; as far as real values are concerned, you would probably be well ahead with a good insurance policy.

On the other hand, there are the lives of you and your loved ones, which—to a drug-crazed burglar—are hardly worth a dime. The recently invaded client who says "money is no object; I want the best," must be (by an ethical man) protected from his own foolishness.

Why are we going into this aspect of intrusion protection now? Primarily, because the detectors selected will have some bearing on the overall system purchased. The sonar or radar detector isn't going to function without proper control circuitry, and you're going to need more than a battery and a bell to get it properly installed and working.

Probably the most common form of intrusion detection in the average home is the momentary-contact switch and latching relay alarm system. This is closely followed by the photoelectric system (Fig. 5-4), with proximity (capacitive) detectors running next. Along with the contact types are the metallic tapes that are used on window glass and on glass doors.

Deterrents

While we are speaking of intrusion, we must not overlook the business of intrusion deterrents, those things that can be done to stop a would-be intruder from even attempting to enter your home. If you reside in a high-crime area, have steel grills placed over the outsides of all windows. Have a pick-proof lock installed on your door. And by all means, get a dog. Anything that hampers the would-be intruder and makes his actions suspicious to neighbors will thwart an illegal entry.

Toward this end, make sure that your locks are used when you exit, and double-lock the doors. When you move into a new

Fig. 5-4. Simple photoelectric intrusion sensor. (Courtesy Walter Kiddie & Co.)

home or apartment, make sure you change all the locks and do not give keys around willy-nilly to maintenance people in the building. Too many others will then have access to your keys, and some maintenance men do a thriving business in selling copies to the netherworld with full instructions on your hours of coming and going. When you're coming home, take a second (that's all it takes) to press your own doorbell, even though nobody's at home. If an intruder is in the house, this will warn him away.

We once were acquainted with a police detective who had a genuine problem. Because of his position, he was naturally the target for every kooky crook trying to make a name. It was kind of like trying to shoot Wyatt Earp. I remember that trying to enter this man's home legally, with him right there, was at least a 10-minute operation during which the most massive key ring I ever saw was brought into play, while assorted locks, bars, guards and protective devices were neutralized. As we mentioned earlier, a well-locked door with properly mounted interior chains and bars serves as a fine deterrent.

But let's talk about lock picking for a moment. There are few good men left who know this art. The usual cylinder lock has five tumblers. Picking consists of placing a hollow locking lug in the key slot and turning it slightly. The pick (a narrow instrument with an end that curves upward) is then inserted in the keyway and the user "feels" for the furthest tumbler. The point of the pick raises this tumbler as far up as it will go and the locking lug is pressed to hold it in the raised position. The next tumbler is elevated, and the next until, when all are raised, the locking lug is able to rotate the cylinder and open the door. As you can see, it is a lengthy procedure. Yet one firm, Dynation, has introduced a cylindrical lock with seven tumblers arranged in a circle. I challenge any but the best to open that lock with picks, and to do it within a reasonable time period.

If the home you're surveying for protection already has an intercom system, by all means take advantage of the current wiring and apply a bit of ingenuity. If a call system is used, all you have to do is wire your sensors across the call circuits so that if any close, all units will activate with the call signal. Before proceeding with an installation where no intercom is in use, it may be wise to suggest to a resident that you can easily install an intercom system at the same time and save the homeowner the cost of additional wiring.

Fig. 5-5. One of nine electric latch types available from the Trine Manufacturing Co.

ELECTRIC LATCHES

The electric latch (Fig. 5-5) is now starting to make vast inroads in residential protection. Originally, the electric latch was used for business offices, where visitors were admitted to inner areas through an electrically latched gate. An employee would press a button, the latch would buzz, and the visitor could open the gate and enter. Such devices are now used in apartment houses, where a tenant identifies a visitor via an intercom, then presses the electric release button, allowing the visitor to push the door open and enter.

Electric latches lend themselves to individual residences as well, and form a locking system that is totally pick-proof. The Detex Company makes such a latch. Here's how it works in a residential application. Visitors can be identified either through a peep hole or by voice, and the resident presses a button, opening the latch. Instead of a key, each member of the family is given a small plastic card with a pattern of magnetic inks printed on it. When the card is inserted in a slot near the door, the electric latch is operated. Such latching systems can be used for locking and unlocking any door, but the general system lends itself even further to the protection of electronic equipment as well. An electric latch system can be wired into your stereo equipment, amateur radio transmitter, or any electrically operated device and it cannot be turned on except with a proper card. Naturally, such a system eliminates the mechanical lock, and activates a latching relay circuit instead. The circuit connects just "downstream" of the on-off switch, which acts as a reset when the card is removed and the equipment is turned off.

Chapter 6

Control Units & System Considerations

The control unit is the heart of any alarm system. Depending on the type of system installed, it takes information from the various detectors and sensors, translates this information and provides a signal of some sort to activate an alarm, activate a telephone dialer with a recorded message, and in more sophisticated installations, illuminate an indicator panel to show the resident where the activity is taking place. Some control units are so cumbersome and complex that they are designed for remote installation and provide for a remote head which offers indicators and-or controls in a more convenient location.

As with any other component part of the overall system, the control unit selected will be chosen on the basis of inputs and outputs. Toward this point, we are often asked about "mixing and matching" of component parts from different manufacturers. Is this a feasible approach? Are there any conditions which justify such an action? And what are the pitfalls if such a course is taken?

Let us analyze these problems. When would you select such a course of action? Most frequently, when a system already installed is to be expanded and you are unable to secure the additional sensors from the original manufacturer. And there can be numerous reasons for this, too. The original dealer who made the installation may not be available to the resident for one reason or another, and you may not be franchised by the manufacturer. Then, too, you may be installing sensors or alarms that the original installation not only did not have but that are not available from that manufacturer. This is frequently the case when you are adding fire and intrusion protection to an existing intercom system.

Under other normal conditions, it is wisest to install sensors and alarms from the same manufacturer that sells the control system, for then you get an integrated system that you know is going to work well. Of course, you may find that you can get a better price on sensors from one, more convenient delivery or terms from another on alarms, and so on. This sort of thing is what gives the technician the edge. If the control circuit, which, as we said, is the heart of the system, calls for open-circuit fire alarm sensors and open-circuit intrusion detectors, you can easily use open-circuit sensors from any other manufacturer, and they should operate with little or no problem.

It's essentially the same with alarm devices. If the output of the control unit is a relay, chances are that all three relay contacts, the contact arm, the normally open and normally closed, are brought out to a terminal strip and you can wire the alarms any way that they require.

The pitfalls of such an action are fairly obvious. Should any fault in the system take place, the individual manufacturers are going to disclaim any responsibility for your not having used their equipment throughout. And your own lawyers may tell you that you're sticking your neck out a mile. But it's been our limited experience that you do this in any case, for when a system fails and there's any room for doubt, the installation is usually blamed first by the manufacturers! Of course, having done the installation, you will probably be in a finger-pointing posture yourself!

The control unit for a given system must, of course, match that system. In the more exotic installations, this means highly specialized units, designed to do specific jobs. It puts this writer in mind of the young amateur radio operator who had a 75-watt transmitter and decided to increase the power. His modification consisted of replacing the final amplifier tube with one capable of handling the higher wattage; however, he made no change whatever in supply power or drive. Result? The same power with a cooler-running tube. The point is that in engineering, you "don't get somethin' for nuthin'." Given a control unit with limited capabilities, don't expect to add a microwave or sonar detecting device and expect it to function. On the other hand, simple relay or switching-type control units are generally all of a sort as far as action goes, and with some measure of ingenuity, you can bend and flex the designs within given parameters.

SYSTEM CAPABILITIES

Often, a resident will evaluate his system and ask some questions about its performance.

"Can I determine, when an alarm sounds, whether the cause is fire or intrusion? How can I tell?"

"Can the system be made to indicate in what part of the house the fire or intrusion has occurred?"

50

Where a control unit is designed only to indicate that a sensor has closed, and does so by sounding an alarm, chances are that while its value may appear limited, any homeowner would rather know about such a closing than be left to find out—the hard way—when flame is out of control or a burglar has done his damage. The idea being that even this seemingly scant information is better—far better—than no information at all.

Yet should a resident desire additional information, it is an easy matter to set up a dual-string system, with intrusion alarms wired to one alarm, fire detectors wired to the other. Add a couple of small pilot lamps, and at least the resident will know whether to call the fire or police department!

Another advantage that you can provide when making an installation is a series of inputs to the control unit from the various sensors. Now you do not need a separate line for each sensor; rather, a simple indication of where in the house the signal emanated from—upstairs or downstairs, the front or the back—is usually sufficient in most cases. Naturally, this means running additional wires and-or cables from various sensors and detectors to the control unit. But it's a factor well-worth considering.

Another question concerns stop-gap security systems. Typical is the overhead sprinkler systems with which we are all familiar. In the event of fire, the heat melts a fusible link which releases a flood of water from the overhead lines. Electronics people are generally opposed to this sort of installation, for the plumbing is rarely attractive, and while a man may be willing to sacrifice aesthetic beauty to protect his home, he generally lives with a woman who is not. At least one manufacturer has produced a foam or soda-acid extinguisher that operates automatically when heat is present. Unfortunately, these systems are rather indiscriminate and soak everything. Better than a fire? Of course!

Attempts have been made, as noted earlier, to thwart intruders with everything from electric shock to tear gas and shotgun shells. But check with your local police and fire departments, and you get a totally different sort of story. This is what we were told, by local representatives of both civil agencies:

In case of fire, regardless of how small and apparently insignificant, your first action, after getting your loved ones out and alerting all residents, is to call the fire department. An attempt to extinguish a fire by yourself is noble to be sure, but if you lose the battle, you have a conflagration. Those first few minutes are precious and can spell the difference. Yet in spite of these warnings, many people learn too late that they should have called for assistance. And assistance doesn't mean your next-door neighbor with his garden hose, either.

One of the most dangerous people is a burglar who is nervous, and all sensible burglars are nervous. The burglar who is not nervous is not sensible either, and that makes him one kind of nut or other. In either case, not the kind you can reasonably deal with. Again, get help as fast as you can, and don't put your life on the line. Nothing that you own is worth that.

LOCAL VERSUS REMOTE CONTROL

It is important to have some idea of where an outbreak (of fire) or an "inbreak" (of intrusion) occurs. This is relatively easy to implement at low cost by adding a siren module and small loudspeaker to the system wherever you have a detector. It can be especially important in the case of a fire.

Take Charlie's installation as an example. He put a heat detector over his boiler and another over his kitchen range. These were connected to a small siren in his bedroom. As with most such installations, once it was made, it was promptly forgotten. Then one day, Charlie and his wife were in the bedroom talking, when the chilling sound of the siren was heard.

"You take the kitchen! I'll take the basement." They both ran. Seeing nothing untoward in the basement, Charlie rushed to meet his wife in the kitchen. Charlie's father-in-law was frying fish and the oil had caught fire. With the fire under control (a lid was placed on the pan) Charlie applied an ice cube to the detector to reset it.

To install an indicating system, it is necessary to have each detector coupled directly to the control unit, where closing the detector (if it is a closing-type or normally open) will activate a relay which in turn will operate the alarm system and an indicator lamp on the monitor board. The monitor board can be placed in the control unit if this is convenient, or it can be remotely mounted with a cable to the control unit.

If it is difficult or inconvenient to use wiring around the home, this writer discovered another way. We were making an installation in a truly modern residence. No wonder they wanted protection: They had "what to protect!" But when we explained that the system was to be interconnected by electric wires, the lady of the house objected. We explained that we would conceal the wiring wherever possible, even offered her a choice of insulation. She didn't want "messy wires" around the house and even (to be frank) objected to the heat sensors, the smoke detector, and the control unit. We knew we were in trouble when she examined the sample heat detectors we had brought along and asked if we had any color other than beige. The installation required 12 detectors, and we left them with her the week before so she could paint them to match her ceilings. (We explained that she mustn't paint the little metallic buttons at the bottom.)

The wireless system we finally installed is a good one, where price isn't too much of an object. We located small transmitters of the citizens band type used for controlling model airplanes. Got them from a local manufacturer for under $10 each. A matching small receiver was placed right in the control unit, and when the sensors closed, the receiver activated the little relay, closing the alarm circuit.

One of our TV dealer friends had a small problem with theft. His shop was hit regularly, especially when he was alone in the store, or not there at all. A customer (actually an ally of the thief) would occupy him over the transistor radios, while the thief was making off with a small television set. He rigged up a system that was inexpensive and we recommend it to you for your consideration.

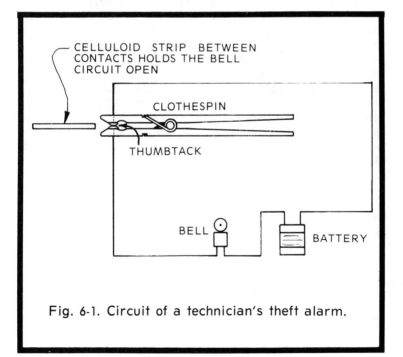

Fig. 6-1. Circuit of a technician's theft alarm.

Spring-type clothespins are fitted with small thumb tacks (the metal kind, with no paint) and the tacks are connected by soldering wires to each tack (Fig. 6-1). One lead goes to a power source (he used a 6-volt battery) the other goes to a large alarm bell, available inexpensively from many war surplus shops. The bell connects to the battery's other terminal. With any pin closed, the tacks make contact and the bell rings.

He wired a small strip of celluloid to each display set in the shop, placing the celluloid strip between the contacts of one of the pins. Each pin was then screwed to the counter, behind the set it was designed to protect. If a would-be thief lifted the set, he'd also pull loose the strip, allowing the contacts to close, and sound the alarm.

Exactly what is it that you want to protect? Naturally, the idea of a thief entering without permission is sufficient reason to want protection. But in many households, it isn't so much the premises that we want to safeguard as it is certain valuables. Needless to say, the clothespin and celluloid system just described can easily serve to protect your valuables without having to go through a complete home-protection system just to do it.

If you stop to consider the motivation that drives people to want protection, you will find that it is a need for security. Couple this with the fact that an obvious control system constantly reminds them about the system, and you've got a conflicting problem. The best control system, then, is one that is unobtrusive, out of sight, and totally invisible until it is needed. This works very well with the purpose of the system, too. You don't necessarily want a would-be thief to know where your system is so he can attempt to bypass it some way or other, do you? Maybe you are proud of the installation job you've done, but you can be proudest when nobody even knows its there!

Chapter 7

How Much Must You "Pay"?

How expensive should a "good system" be? How much must it cost to install full protection for you, your family, or your place of business? If you want a dollars-and-cents figure, we can't produce such figures in even a general way. But in deciding on an installation, or in helping to evaluate the extent to which you ought to go in making an installation, take a few things into careful consideration.

Consider, for example, the alternatives to fire or illegal entry. If you should be hit with a fire, chances are that you will lose valued property that cannot easily be replaced, regardless of how much money you have tied up in assorted fire insurance policies. Then there's the factor of life itself. How much dollar value would you put on your own life? That of your family? And don't overlook the cost of having an all-out conflagration in your home. It's a traumatic shock that you will never forget.

It's about the same when a forced entry occurs. When a burglar breaks and enters, he's doing so with a definite purpose in mind. A theft is little enough problem, for while most material items can be readily replaced, there's always the danger to life and limb. And again, the fact that you have been burglarized is frightening. The safety and sanctity of your home has been penetrated, and you can't consider yourself totally safe again.

AFTER THE HORSE RUNS AWAY

Most people make their first real investment in protective devices after they've been "hit." "This," they say, "will never be allowed to happen to me again."

Oddly enough, those who have lived through a fire or a housebreaking are never difficult to convince that they need protection. It's the chap who anticipates such an action who takes a lot of convincing.

Full protection is a combination of words that is purely subjective. Where, exactly, do you draw the line? Is detecting a fire and sounding an alarm protection enough? Or do you want to provide a means of controlling the fire until help arrives? Do you want to summon help merely by sounding a bell and alerting the occupants and neighbors? Or do you want to call the fire department automatically as well? In case of a burglary, do you simply plan to alert the resident that an entry has been effected? Or do you want to summon help? Notify the police? Scare off the perpetrator?

"PROTECTION" vs FULL PROTECTION

The difference between "protection" and "full protection" can be a matter of degree. In the event of a fire, a full-protection system should be one that senses the presence of combustion, contains it, muffles it and controls it without waking you up. In case of illegal entry, full protection can mean the detection and safe entrapment of a would-be thief. But how automatic need you get? Your purpose is to protect a family by notifying them sufficiently in advance that there is danger present. They, once apprised of the situation, can take appropriate action.

One instance that took place recently involved a young lady, living alone, who had a system installed. It was a fairly simple installation, and as she explained to a visiting friend while the installer was doing his work, "If a burglar opens a window or door, or if a fire breaks out, this bell will start to ring. When that happens, it wakes me up."

"Then what do you do?" asker her friend.

"I dunno" she replied, shrugging her shoulders, "scream, I guess."

Any installer of such systems should make an evaluation of the premises and make careful recommendations to the residents. Is there ample facility for escape from any given room in which an occupant might be trapped? If not, a rope escape ladder might be called for. Are the residents carefully instructed in proper emergency procedures? Is suitable equipment available for the protection of the family when an alarm sounds an alert?

PROPERTY INVENTORY

One tremendous sales aid for the installer-consultant is a printed form that can be left with the resident so he can make a total inventory of his property. On this form, he should list all property of real value and the dollar value of each piece. An inventory must be prepared on a room-by-room basis, and in that form, it serves many purposes. First of all, every homeowner should have such an inventory of his possessions, for this enables him to properly know and evaluate his worth. As an interesting experiment, ask him to inventory his possessions without actually checking them on a separate sheet. He'll usually be quite amazed at how much he omitted. The truth of the matter is that when his insurance company asks him to provide an inventory, it will be under similar circumstances, assuming that property is now gone due to fire or theft.

Finally, this property inventory provides the resident with the big overall dollar figure right there in front of him, and this is what he will have at the back of his mind while you are quoting prices for his protection!

AN OUNCE OF PREVENTION

While we are obviously all agreed that protection is essential, make the point quite clearly to your client that electronic protective devices are an adjunct, not a cure-all. He should by no means drop his insurance policies the day that the installation is completed. On the other hand, he should contact his insurance agent and advise him that he has installed protective devices, with the idea of reducing his premiums.

There's hardly a better deterrent to burglary than a good system of door and windows locks. Make the job of entering tougher and one that takes too long to accomplish, and you've got a great foothold on the battle. You see, too much emphasis must not be placed on the function of the system itself, for there are other factors involved. We mention this, because as sure as shootin', you're going to be asked—sooner or later—to advise on the subject of door and window locks as deterrents and as adjuncts to the system you sell and install.

What are the things that a would-be burglar is afraid of? Primarily, he is afraid of being apprehended. The first step toward apprehension is discovery, and anything you can do to make him think he risks apprehension, is going to make your property more secure. The sounding of an alarm is usually enough to drive a would-be thief away. This can be anything from a bell or siren that sounds with his first attempts, or the barking of a dog. When he knows he has no business on your property and must spend an inordinate amount of time fooling with locks and chains, or disabling a system, he knows he will arouse suspicion from neighbors.

But, of course, the would-be burglar is not always a madman or a fool, either. There are certain wise things a homeowner should do prior to leaving on a protracted journey.

Stop milk, and mail and newspaper deliveries. There's nothing quite like a pile-up of these things at the door to alert a would-be thief when he's casing a neighborhood for possible candidates.

Notify the neighbors of your trip. Some recent robberies consisted of backing a small panel truck to the driveway and brazenly removing household goods in broad daylight. Neighbors thought these "movers" were expected, for they gained entry with ease, acted with impunity. Leave a light. A fully-darkened house is an invitation that says "nobody's home."

But as we said, all burglars are not complete fools. You can bet your bottom dollar that while you are reading this book for your own information, many a smart thief is reading it as well. Thieves have also studied the police advisories, and they are well aware that you will stop the mail, newspaper and milk deliveries before your trip; that you will leave a light, probably one of those inexpensive photoelectric light turner-oners. So you've got to think a little smarter.

Charlie is a crook that we interviewed in the Men's House of Detention in New York City. Charlie is a professional thief, who makes his living by burglarizing suburban homes. He generally goes to work in a car, drives through suburban streets at dusk, looking for suitable "hits." Charlie thinks like a crook, acts like a crook, and knows as much about intrusion protection as anybody in the business.

"I don't go barging in. I watch a house for a couple of nights. If I see only one light lit in only one room night after night, I figure the family is really away. One place I cracked, the guy really figured he was clever. He had an electric timer that was turning lights on and off in different parts of the house all night long. What a setup this guy had. Damn house was going on and off like a pin-ball machine.

"In 'nother place, the guy had window shades down, and I could see people dancing. Shadows on the shade. Could hear the music, too. Peeked in through another window, and the guy had a phonograph going in front of the window, with a lamp behind the phonograph. He had two cardboard cutouts of a man and a woman sitting on the turntable, and the shadow of them on the shade made it look like a party inside. There was a party inside, too. Me."

What Charlie didn't want—ever—was "trouble." "I'm just tryin' to make a living. If I get busted, I go up for a couple years and lose my income until I come out again. Who needs it? I don't play games, either. I don't want no trouble. If I get an idea that there's somebody at home, or if there's a burglar alarm system, I don't play games. There's enough houses without. What do I need this for? If you think I'm gonna take a chance trying to figure how to beat your system when the guy next door ain't got no protection at all, you're crazy.

"I don't want no trouble. I guess you know that the crook doesn't keep what he steals. What am I gonna do with cameras, televisions and jewels? I have to convert that stuff to money, so I sell it to a fence. You go out and buy a $400 television set, right? So do I get $400 for it? I'm lucky if the fence gives me $25 for the set. He can sell it then for a lot more, but he doesn't get $400 either. Anybody that wants to buy a television set for $400 can buy it the same place you did. A guy buys a hot set, he doesn't know what condition it's in, he's taking a chance. So he only pays maybe a hundred for it. Maybe a hundred fifty, right? A smart guy parlays his luck against me. He buys electronic protection, gets a dog, and he buys homeowner insurance."

We asked Charlie if he would fight when he's caught.

"Fight? Who me? I look like Mohammed Ali? Come on. I don't need no trouble. (Charlie is slight of build.) Even if I try to defend myself, I got a disadvantage. The guy in the house, he knows if he's got a gun. I don't. If I hit him one, he gets mad and pulverizes me, then tells the cops I broke his nose. All I want to do is beat it. I once jumped out a window and got away."

We asked Charlie to offer some advice to his would-be "hit" so they could defend their homes against him and others like him.

"Come on fella. Look. What do you do for a living, huh? You're a writer? Would you go out and tell the whole world what you're writing about so someone can beat you to it? This is free enterprise, ain't it? Look. I'm here waiting for my trial. I'm guilty, and they got a good case against me. They caught me red-handed, got all kinds of witnesses. My hit already collected from his insurance company, and the insurance company lawyers are pushing the case. My lawyer? He just got out of law school and was appointed by the court. He hasn't got a chance. So I'll get sent up again, maybe three to five with time off for good behavior. Maybe I'll get paroled. When I come out, I gotta make a living again, right? And you want me to tell my hits how to keep me from making a living? You get no information from me pal. I'll be out soon, and making my rounds again."

We left a nearly full pack of cigarettes with Charlie and went back out into the sun. You see, it's like Charlie says... he'll be out again soon.

Chapter 8

Commercial Equipment

The best way for you to find out what's available in fire and intrusion alarm protection systems is to shop. Unfortunately, not all of us are easily able to run around looking at what there is to be had. Still, the very first thing you'll want to do is familiarize yourself, and toward this end, we think we've found a unique way to help. Working closely with the editorial staff of RADIO-ELECTRONICS Magazine, we gathered lists of the leading manufacturers of this type of equipment and wrote to them. Each submitted complete data on their own systems for inclusion in this book. We have carefully analyzed the material supplied and the results follow.

Whether you are planning to install a system in your own home, go into the business of protection, or just want to know what's available, this section of the book will help you immeasurably. If you plan to design and build a system of your own, you will find many valuable tips here, for in addition to providing you with some well-thought-out ideas, you will also find equipment listed that you can purchase. Frequently, such equipment works better, looks better, and costs less than anything you might whip up on the workbench. But before we consider the ready-to-operate units, let's look at a kit-type system currently available.

BUILD-IT-YOURSELF KIT

The Heath Company offers a home protection system in kit form which you assemble and install yourself. It functions in a manner similar to the wireless intercoms that use the house wiring as a transmission medium. Basically, the system is composed of three separate circuits that can be added to and expanded upon to give you the most complete protection available.

The receiver-alarm box contains a warning device or alarm. A remotely located smoke-heat detector-transmitter signals and triggers the receiver alarm when smouldering or open fires occur. The utility detector-transmitter signals a mass of other conditions, including intrusion, fire, temperature changes or flooding. The three basic units are illustrated in Fig. 8-1.

Intrusion is detected by a system of magnetic reed switches that are recessed into doors and jambs or window frames and tracks. Preset thermo devices warn of changing temperature conditions, and are handy for protecting your freezer among other things. The flood condition detectors can warn of "overactive" swimming pool conditions, flooding in your water pump, etc. Since the system operates from the

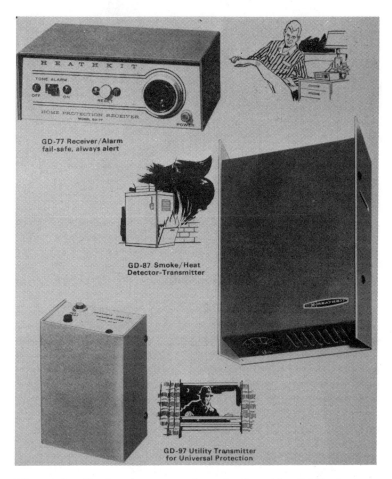

Fig. 8-1. Basic components of the Heathkit home-protection system.

Fig. 8-2. View of the Heathkit Model GD-77 receiver interior.

power wiring, it also indicates when there's been a power failure.

One of the nicer features of this system is that there are no unsightly wires to string around. Installation is, for the most part, only a matter of plugging in. In fact, where more than one receiver alarm is required (you may find it an advantage to have receivers in two different rooms) simply buy the additional unit and plug it into the line in whatever room is convenient.

The receiver (Fig. 8-2) is a fail-safe unit in that it contains a rechargeable nickel-cadmium battery. This takes over during a power failure and signals the loss of primary power. The smoke-heat detector transmitter should be mounted high on a wall in areas where conflagrations can occur. In the base of the unit are slots to permit the easy entry of smoke to the actual detector; a heat-sensing unit is also mounted on the base. Additional heat sensors can be connected by wire to the transmitter and placed wherever convenient or necessary. Power for this unit is drawn from the standard house wiring. If smoke occurs or the temperature increases to 133 degrees F, the alarm will sound.

The utility transmitter unit can be used with any of a number of sensors, including several you may think up yourself. Any sensing device that provides either an open or closed circuit will actuate this unit and trigger the alarm. There are five remote inputs at the back of the transmitter, and any number of sensors can be connected into these (voltage is 24 or less). Also built into the transmitter is a warning signal that indicates an internal component failure or a break in one of the sensor lines. More than one transmitter can be used as well, and an indicator lamp on each transmitter serves as an indication of which transmitter is sending an alarm.

Sensors

The sensors you select are determined by the type of malfunction you wish to detect. Fire sensors are simple thermal buttons that close a circuit when an elevated temperature is reached. Cold sensors can best be obtained from freezer servicing centers where these specialized thermostatic switches are readily available at low cost. Temperature-change sensors are ordinary home thermostats that are wired to the utility transmitter and signal an increase or decrease in ambient room temperature.

The intrusion detectors are simple magnetic reed switches, consisting of metallic leaves encased in glass sleeves, sealed at both ends. The switches are activated when a magnet is brought close to the glass envelope. To install these sensors, the switch must be mounted in a door frame, the magnet in the edge of the door, directly parallel with it. In this way, the switch will activate when the door is opened or closed. In a window, the switch is placed in the window track, the magnet in the window frame. As you can see, the switch is always mounted in the fixed portion, while the magnet is located in the operable part. This makes wiring simpler, and reduces flexing of the wiring once the unit is installed.

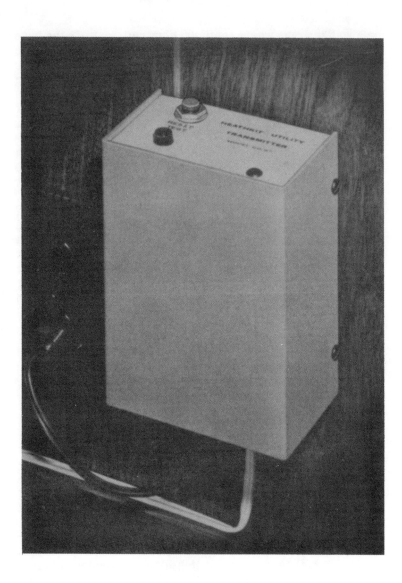

Fig. 8-3. Heathkit Model GD-97 utility transmitter shown with external sensors connected.

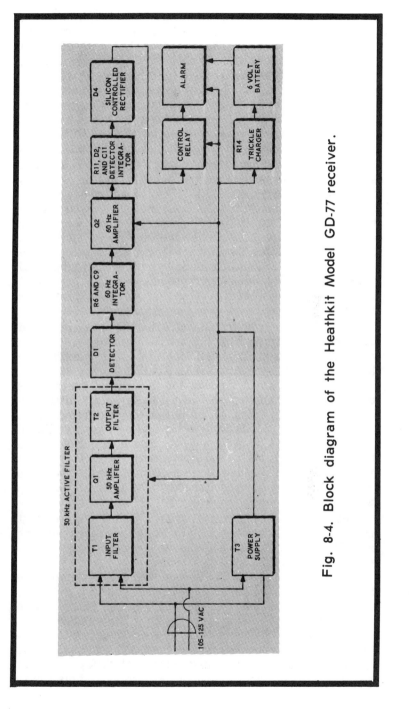

Fig. 8-4. Block diagram of the Heathkit Model GD-77 receiver.

65

The installation of these sensors is relatively simple. Use a small wood chisel to rout out the space you need. Take out sufficient material so the sensor will be flush with the wood surface, and the same with the magnet. These units function most positively when the magnet operates very close to the switch. Where wiring is to be introduced, use a V-blade chisel to rout a path for the wiring. A few strategically placed drops of cement will hold the sensor, actuator magnet and wiring in place. When the cement has dried, a bit of wood filler and a touch with sandpaper will complete the installation.

In some cases, a light beam makes a fine sensor, too. You can use any standard photoelectric detection system with this transmitter; simply wire the output connections of the photoelectric detector to the transmitter. If you use a photoelectric system, it's wise to place the light source and detector at the same side of the room and use a well-placed mirror to reflect the beam back from the source to the detector. In addition to eliminating the need for additional convenience outlets, this system provides a double beam that gives you a second chance at an intruder who may have missed the first beam.

As you can see from the photographs, the units are indeed handsome, in keeping with the usual Heath design. To understand how a typical system operates, let's examine the block diagram for the receiver in Fig. 8-4.

The AC line provides power for the unit, of course. The power line AC is applied also to a 50-kHz active filter consisting of an input filter, an amplifier and an output filter. This, in turn, feeds a diode detector and a passive 60-Hz integrator. The next stage is a 60-Hz active amplifier which applies the signal to a passive detector-integrator and from there to a silicon controlled rectifier. This applies the signal to a control relay and thence to the alarm, a solid-state device in itself.

The line also provides power for a trickle charger that keeps the nickel-cadmium battery at the correct operating level. The battery voltage is applied to the alarm, should there be a power failure.

The block diagram for the smoke-heat transmitter is shown in Fig. 8-5. The power line provides primary voltage to the secondary supplies and the SCR switch. This, in turn, provides power to the module which contains the 50-kHz multivibrator and the load switch. The smoke-detection unit is wired across the relay and between the 325-volt supply and the SCR switch. Its light source and the fail-safe bridging circuit are connected between the 12.6-volt AC supply and the smoke

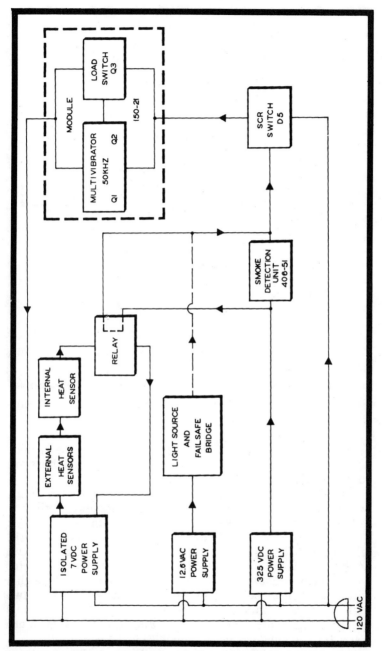

Fig. 8-5. Block diagram of the Heathkit Model GD-87 smoke-heat detector transmitter.

67

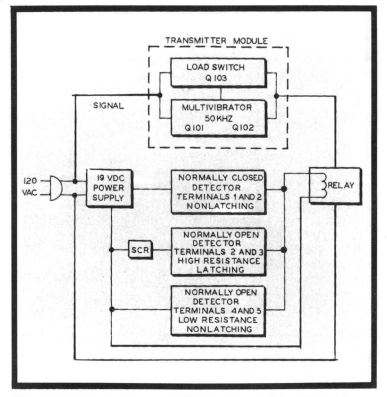

Fig. 8-6. Block diagram of the Heathkit utility transmitter.

detector. The isolated 7-volt DC supply connects to the various heat sensors, one of which is internal to the unit, and these are connected, as in the relay, to the supply.

The utility transmitter circuit (Fig. 8-6) is also fed by the power mains and contains a transmitter module similar to that found in the smoke-heat detector; namely, a 50-kHz multivibrator and a load switch. A 19-volt power supply works off the mains, which feeds a normally closed detector with two nonlatching terminals. It also feeds a normally open detector with two low-resistance nonlatching terminals, and, through a silicon controlled rectifier, a normally open detector with two high-resistance nonlatching terminals. The output relay coils are operated by the three detectors, and relay contacts return a signal (through the transmit module) to the power lines.

A typical installation is shown in Fig. 8-7. The nice thing about the Heath system is its flexibility. You can choose any part or as many parts as you care to implement in your own particular installation. Incidently, pressure switches, such as those rubber hoses that ring bells when you drive into a service station, can also be used across your driveway to signal the arrival of guests—welcome or unwelcome—at your home! Microswitches can be used the way the magnetic reed switches are used to provide additional signals as you need them.

All in all, this is a thorough system and one that offers a maximum of flexibility with ease of installation. Solid-state reliability is offered as well, and the unit's fail-safe feature makes it an outstanding value, whether you plan an installation in your own home or are making installations on a custom basis.

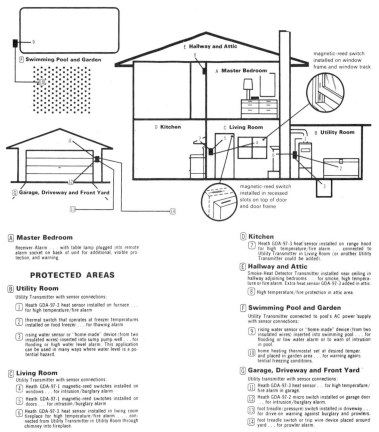

[A] Master Bedroom

Receiver-Alarm . . . with table lamp plugged into remote alarm socket on back of unit for additional, visible protection, and warning.

PROTECTED AREAS

[B] Utility Room

Utility Transmitter with sensor connections:

[1] Heath GDA-97-3 heat sensor installed on furnace . . . for high temperature/fire alarm

[2] thermal switch that operates at freezer temperatures installed on food freezer . . . for thawing alarm

[3] rising water sensor or "home-made" device (from two insulated wires) inserted into sump pump well . . . for flooding or high water level alarm. This application can be used in many ways where water level is a potential hazard.

[C] Living Room

Utility Transmitter with sensor connections:

[4] Heath GDA-97-1 magnetic-reed switches installed on windows . . . for intrusion/burglary alarm

[5] Heath GDA-97-1 magnetic-reed switches installed on doors . . . for intrusion/burglary alarm

[6] Heath GDA-97-3 heat sensor installed in living room fireplace for high temperature/fire alarm . . . connected from Utility Transmitter in Utility Room through chimney into fireplace.

[D] Kitchen

[7] Heath GDA-97-3 heat sensor installed on range hood for high temperature/fire alarm . . . connected to Utility Transmitter in Living Room (or another Utility Transmitter could be added).

[E] Hallway and Attic

Smoke-Heat Detector Transmitter installed near ceiling in hallway adjoining bedrooms . . . for smoke, high temperature or fire alarm. Extra heat sensor GDA-97-3 added in attic.

[8] High temperature/fire protection in attic area.

[F] Swimming Pool and Garden

Utility Transmitter connected to pool's AC power supply with sensor connections:

[9] rising water sensor or "home-made" device (from two insulated wires) inserted into swimming pool . . . for flooding or low water alarm or to warn of intrusion in pool.

[10] home heating thermostat set at desired temper. and placed in garden area . . . for warning against potential freezing conditions.

[G] Garage, Driveway and Front Yard

Utility transmitter with sensor connections:

[11] Heath GDA-97-3 heat sensor . . . for high temperature/fire alarm in garage.

[12] Heath GDA-97-2 micro switch installed on garage door . . . for intrusion/burglary alarm.

[13] foot treadle (pressure) switch installed in driveway . . . for drive-on warning against burglary and prowlers.

[14] foot treadle switch or trip wire device placed around yard . . . for prowler alarm.

Fig. 8-7. Virtually any area of a home can be protected with the Heathkit system.

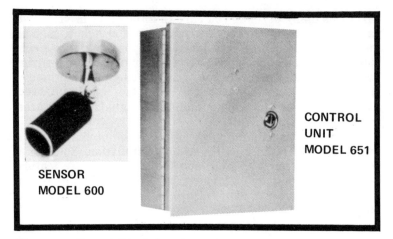

CONTROL
UNIT
MODEL 651

SENSOR
MODEL 600

Fig. 8-8. One ADL intrusion alarm system uses an infrared detector that senses heat from an intruder's body.

READY-TO-OPERATE EQUIPMENT

The remainder of the book is devoted to a description of available equipment, representing the leading manufacturers in the field today. Rather than attempt to categorize the material according to function, we present it in alphabetical order according to manufacturer to avoid duplication, since some manufacturers supply equipment in more than one category.

ADVANCED DEVICES LABORATORY, INC.

ADL has two intrusion alarm systems. The first we will discuss is an infrared detector (Fig. 8-8) that responds to the heat emanating from a burglar's body; no hidden beam is needed. The single sensor mechanism is passive, reacting to the stimulation from external sources. Each sensor secures an area 20 feet by 20 feet, will not react to normal changes in ambient temperature (-30 to +140 degrees F) and operates off a rechargeable power pack in the event of power failure.

As many as eight sensors can be used in one room, and no phasing is required between them. As noise, sound, light or radio interference cause no indication to this unit, it is recommended where other types, subject to such interference, are inadequate. Installation is simple, just a low-voltage hookup between the sensor and control box. The alarm relay contacts provide 115v AC or 28v DC at 2 amps.

The other ADL system is a microwave type. It senses movement in a room under surveillance by any object larger than a cat, moving at a speed of more than one inch per second! Just try looking at your watch and move at a speed of less than one inch per second. Now try to remove an electric typewriter from the room at that speed.

The microwave intruder detector (Fig. 8-9) is a one-piece, solid-state microwave radio transmitter and receiver. It generates a microwave energy field which pulsates at 10.5-billion cycles per second. The shape of the energy field can be adjusted to fill a long, narrow corridor (up to 300 feet long) (Fig. 8-10) or a 10,000-square-foot room (or any shape in between, Fig. 8-11). If any object larger than a cat enters the field, the object's movement is detected and the microwave intruder detector initiates a silent or audible alarm. The microwave intruder detector can be concealed in a small loudspeaker cabinet on the wall, or in some installations its energy beam can be transmitted through the ceiling of a room. And even if an intruder managed to use some electronic gadget to detect the presence of the energy field, he couldn't disable the detector without turning in an alarm.

ADT: AMERICAN DISTRICT TELEGRAPH CO.

ADT offers a complex of protective systems that are suitable for a wide range of applications. You'll find all sorts of

Fig. 8-9. ADL Model 205 microwave intruder detector.

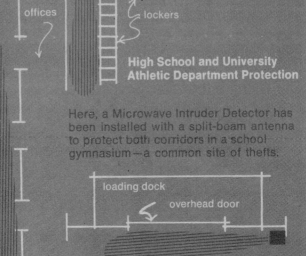

offices

lockers

**High School and University
Athletic Department Protection**

Here, a Microwave Intruder Detector has
been installed with a split-beam antenna
to protect both corridors in a school
gymnasium—a common site of thefts.

loading dock

overhead door

Overhead Door Trap Protection

This loading dock overhead door is
protected against intruders by a
Microwave Intruder Detector. Note that
the energy beam is not pointed directly at
the door, because movement of the door
caused by wind could trigger a false
alarm. Instead, the beam is directed so
that an alarm would be triggered once the
door was opened and the intruder
entered the building.

Long, Narrow Corridor Protection

In this installation, the Microwave Intruder Detector has been
adjusted to produce an energy field 300 feet long and only
a few feet wide to fill the corridor shown. An intruder entering
the corridor from either end or through doors or the walls
would instantly be detected.

Fig. 8-10. Three unique applications of the ADL
microwave intruder detector.

detectors here, including waterflow detectors that signal when water is present; a sprinkler supervisory device that keeps a continuous check on the elements of a sprinkler system; an automatic temperature rate-of-rise detector; a manual fire alarm service that summons firemen quickly when a glass is broken; burglar alarm devices that operate with standard wiring, foil and invisible-ray and ultrasonics; safe and vault protectors that operate with capacitive action or sound detectors; concealed signals to alert police in case of burglary, etc. They've even got a vibration detecting device that protects walls and doors from attack. Photoelectric systems are available from this firm, so that an invisible beam of light stands guard all night.

The ADT system also serves industry with devices that inform plant personnel when equipment stops functioning, when liquids or other materials raise or lower in bins and

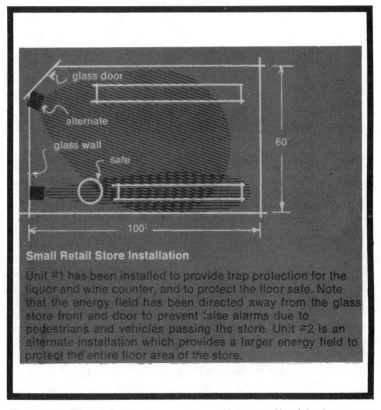

Fig. 8-11. The ADL microwave unit is applicable in more conventional situations, too.

Fig. 8-12. The "Telapproach" burglar alarm uses an electrostatic field to sense the presence of an intruder.

hoppers to critical points, and they even have temperature monitors as well. These systems are available with rechargeable batteries that guarantee fail-safe operation. Should a power failure occur, the internal battery takes over and continues to operate until primary power is restored, following which the built-in battery proceeds to recharge itself, waiting for the next power failure.

One of the prime services offered by this firm is a central office monitoring system, where the alarm devices alert on duty personnel during an emergency. They dispatch assistance when and where it is needed. Of course, you have to be sufficiently close to the central office to warrant such an installation. While the firm has offices in most metropolitan areas, those who are not located near a large, serviced city can still benefit from the local-alarm installations that this firm can provide.

From ADT, you can also get some excellent continuous camera monitoring equipment that regularly photographs the premises. In more than one instance, a would-be burglar has been clearly photographed during his burglary and without his knowledge. This sort of action makes identification a snap for the authorities, and it's awfully hard for the crook to deny his presence when his trial comes up!

"Telapproach" Burglar Alarm

The "Telapproach" burglar alarm system deprives burglars of the time they need to crack a safe. When the

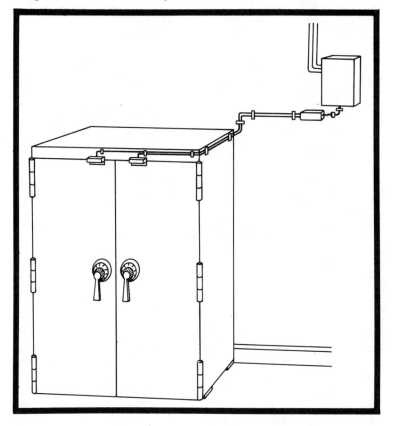

Fig. 8-13. Typical "Telapproach" burglar alarm installation.

Fig. 8-14. Foil stripping used to protect doors and windows.

protection is applied, the system completely encircles the safe area, as illustrated in Fig. 8-12, with an electrostatic field. Any intrusion into this field disturbs the electronic balance of the circuit, causing the detection system to transmit an alarm. The sensitivity can be adjusted to detect an intruder before he can even touch the safe or protected object. Obviously, the system may be used to protect almost any valuable possession or a specific area, such as a stairway, doorway, etc.—where the detection of unauthorized entrance is desired.

The electronic capacitance field surrounding the protected object cannot be detected by the human senses. The system can be combined with other burglar alarm services. Fig. 8-13 shows a typical installation.

In commercial ADT installations, doors, transoms and show windows are protected by foil stripping (Fig. 8-14). Doors and movable-sash windows are also safeguarded by contacts that operate to transmit an alarm if they are opened. Immovable windows may be protected by foil or fine wires running through wooden screens made of ⅜" doweling, closely spaced. Entry cannot be made without cutting through the doweling and wires. Walls, ceilings and floors may be similarly protected by concealed wires.

The "Vibralarm" vibration detector (Fig. 8-15) is designed to reinforce the protection afforded by standard ADT premises burglar alarm equipment. It operates as the result of vibrations caused by attacks on the surface to which it is attached. The detector is most valuable as a measure of protection against attack through walls, ceilings and extensive glass surfaces, which are often difficult or expensive to protect by conventional means.

The ADT devices shown here were selected as a means of adding to our overall spectrum of alarm system descriptions, not as a representation of ADT services.

Fig. 8-15. ADT "Vibralarm" vibration detector senses any physical disturbance inflicted on a door or window.

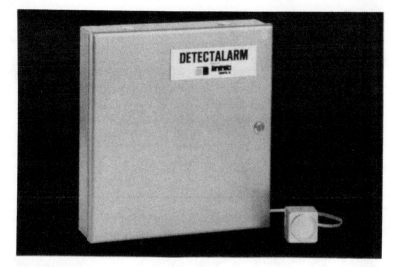

Fig. 8-16. Alarmtronics' "Detectalarm" sound sensing intrusion unit.

ALARMTRONICS ENGINEERING, INC.

This firm offers two systems that are significant for our purposes here. The first is the audio detection system, which operates on the premise that an intruder will make noise. He can't help it. Whether the noise occurs during his initial break-in, or after it, noise that doesn't belong in the area will be there.

The system takes into account any ambient noise, and disregards or cancels it. Noise that is not natural triggers the alarm system. It's an ideal way to handle stay-behinds, also—those would-be thieves who hide themselves in the premises of a store or shop before closing time, and then, after ransacking the place, break out rather than break in.

The "Detectalarm" is designed to monitor all internal space, or selected portions, of one building or a complex of buildings. Using low-voltage wiring, it will utilize existing public address or paging speakers or its own microphone audio sensors. The Model AE-1, shown in Fig. 8-16, has a control to adjust the sensitivity of the sound detection circuit, as well as a control to vary the sensitivity of the cancellation circuit. There is also a control to adjust the number of seconds required to trigger the alarm, these occurring within 30 seconds of time. The number is adjustable from 3 to 10, with a minimum half second between sound pulses. Another control varies the time (one second to 2 minutes) that the alarm is triggered and then automatically reset. Supplementary sensors can be added to detect fire smoke, flooding, and to monitor freezers.

The "Detectalarm" Micro-X is an X-band microwave motion sensor with an adjustable coverage of 100 to 8,000 square feet. It can be wall-mounted on a ball-joint bracket (Fig. 8-17) or disguised as a wall speaker, a book or a desk, etc. The manufacturer says its operation is not affected by air turbulence, noise, RF interference, birds, or insects.

Fig. 8-18 shows a typical industrial installation using "Detectalarm" sound sensors, plus auxiliary fire sensors and door contacts.

The second system, and one whose novelty is most intriguing, is an infrared photoelectric system that we would defy anybody to locate. There are no "black boxes" to make a thief suspect, and no curious wiring to attract his attention. There are, however, a couple of simple, standard duplex wall

Fig. 8-17. The "Detectalarm" Micro-X uses a microwave field to sense movement.

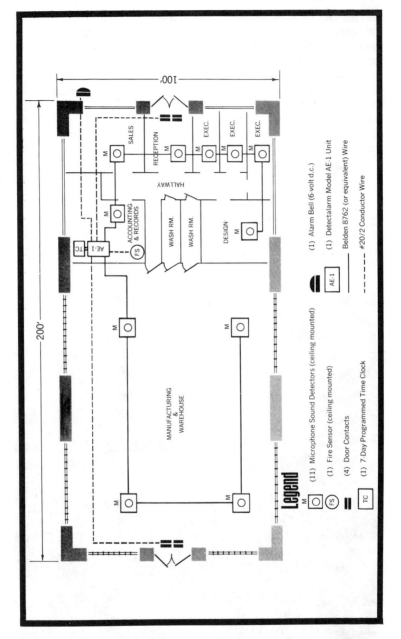

Fig. 8-18. Diagram of a typical industrial installation using "Detectalarm" sound sensors and auxiliary fire sensors and door contacts.

outlets (Fig. 8-19), directly opposite each other. These can even be equipped with cord-and-plug sets to further allay suspicion, and make them appear to be in normal use. But take a close look at the grounding contacts—that's where all the action is. The transmitter button simply makes a small indicator lamp that offers an infrared light which is invisible to the naked eye. The system has a useful range up to 75 feet.

The Mini-Sentry system is not subject to noise or vibration levels normally encountered in any residential or industrial environment. Further, the infrared beam is modulated, a

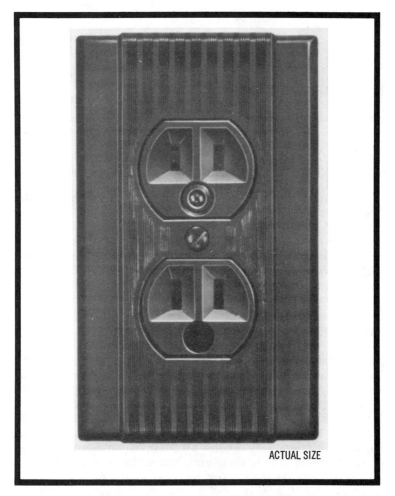

ACTUAL SIZE

Fig. 8-19. Closed view of the "Mini-Sentry" infrared Alarmtronics intrusion detector.

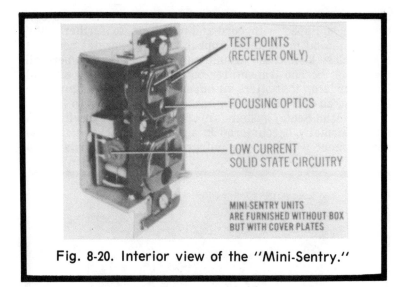

Fig. 8-20. Interior view of the "Mini-Sentry."

feature which prevents the sending of false alarms which could be caused by lightning flashes, flickering sunlight, and so on.

Various models of the Mini-Sentry are designed for battery operation or AC operation with battery standby capability. This means that property remains under surveillance even during extended power failures or a deliberate interruption of power. The current drain of the system is very slight. With battery operation, at least one full year of maintenance-free service can be obtained. Fig. 8-20 is an interior view of the unit.

ARROWHEAD ENTERPRISES, INC.

Photoelectric systems dominate the Arrowhead line. In addition to light sources and receivers, you'll find mirrors and infrared windows which provide an invisible light beam. Mirrors are fully adjustable. There's one intriguing aspect to Arrowhead's equipment line: Not only are their units designed to fit into standard wall convenience outlets, but in such installations they become all but invisible. Standard wall-outlet plates used over these units add to the appearance.

Units are available for surface mounting (Fig. 8-21), recess mounting (Fig. 8-22), and the receptacle box installation (Fig. 8-23). They are operable at ranges up to 200 feet. The receptacle-mount models produce two infrared

RECEIVER
(with add't'n'l protective bracket)

TRANSMITTER

Fig. 8-21. Arrowhead Model 1000 infrared intrusion detector designed for surface mounting.

Model 1100-1 Recess Box   Model 1100-2 Recess Box With IR Window

Fig. 8-22. The Model 1100 shown mounted in recess boxes.

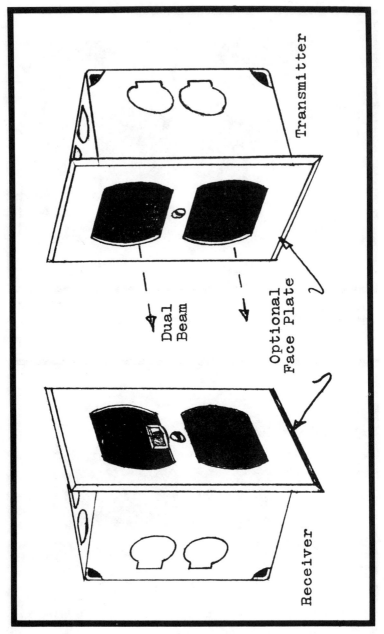

Fig. 8-23. Several Arrowhead models are designed for receptacle mounting. Two infrared beams are used for added reliability.

beams for added reliability. The DC power supply and transmitter are built into a double-gang wall outlet box, or a separate remote power supply, also contained in a double outlet box, is available. With adjustable mirrors (Fig. 8-24), you can bounce the light beam to angles of up to 90 degrees to provide maximum area coverage.

Fig. 8-25 illustrates Arrowhead's freezer alarm system. The sensor unit ignores "defrost" cycles but detects the beginning of temperature rise, caused by a malfunction, before the stored food is affected. The sensor utilizes a thermistor, a solid-state temperature sensor, and a unique (patent applied for) technique for achieving the required time delay without the use of any moving parts. The annunciator uses a

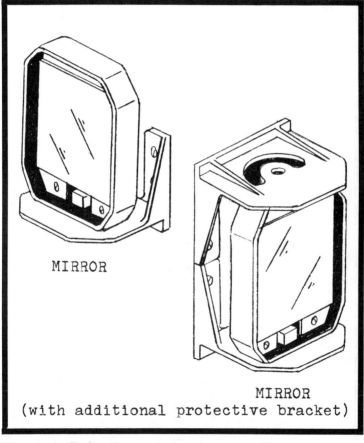

MIRROR

MIRROR
(with additional protective bracket)

Fig. 8-24. Reflecting mirrors increase the range of a system.

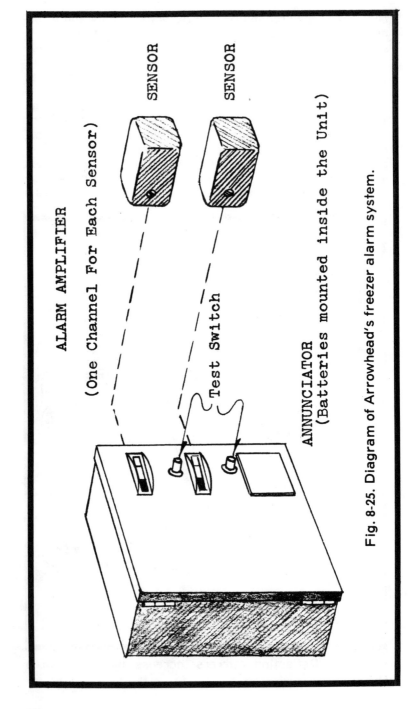

Fig. 8-25. Diagram of Arrowhead's freezer alarm system.

SENSOR

SENSOR

ALARM AMPLIFIER

(One Channel For Each Sensor)

Test Switch

ANNUNCIATOR
(Batteries mounted inside the Unit)

transistor amplifier for the alarm. The amplifier operates on a single 1.5v no. 6 dry cell for more than a year. The only moving part in the system is the alarm relay. The time delay is optimized by an adjustment in the alarm amplifier. The system in Fig. 8-25 will protect two freezers.

The Arrowhead stop-action photographic system consists of a panoramic sweep camera with 50mm, high-resolution lens and automatic drive unit (Fig. 8-26A) together with a choice of the following options. Camera is available with remote control (Fig. 8-26B), local control or hold up options with a choice of automatic or manual exposure controls and with or without standby rechargeable battery power. The camera may be adjusted to sweep in any arc up to 180 degrees. Operates continuously at preset exposure intervals and-or on command from any location. Remote control and local control units feature an exposure interval selector, scan indicator, film footage and battery voltage indicators encased in a rugged,

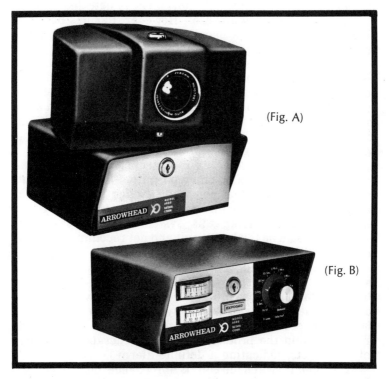

(Fig. A)

(Fig. B)

Fig. 8-26. Arrowhead automatic-exposure camera surveillance system, available with an automatic drive unit (A) or remote control (B).

tamper-proof housing. Supervised, rechargeable standby power is also available which operates the camera even when normal power fails. Film is easily loaded into removable cassettes.

THE ARTRONIX SURVEILLANCE SYSTEM

This is a microwave doppler system designed to check for movement. Properly installed, the system covers the area from wall-to-wall, floor-to-ceiling. The protective radar waves will operate through nonmetallic walls as well, providing protection for more than one room.

You may have heard that intrusion alarm systems are fallible, in that a commercial premise, so protected, has had its alarm triggered by a small animal or rodent, with the result that the owner is called out in the middle of the night. Obviously, with some systems this can happen, especially a system such as this, in which movement is detected without the need for triggering a sensor. However, this has been anticipated by the Artronix people, and the movement of small animals will not trigger the device.

Nevertheless, the system is highly sensitive, and if there is a small sign that is free to flap in the breeze, this flapping will be sufficient to sound the alarm. Obviously, it is scarcely the system that one would install where passersby outside a store might innocently sound the alarm, nor is it the kind of system to be used in a private home where family members are free to wander around during a sleepless night!

But if you are thinking about protecting an area that can be locked at night, with no entry permitted for anybody, this could well be the system you want. Notice that the sensor (antenna—a one-foot aluminum rod) and control system are in one box, and modifying this system to incorporate fire protection would be fairly difficult and not recommended. For fire protection, a separate system is advised.

The "Space Switch," Model 7100 (Fig. 8-27) is a solid-state microwave radar system operating in the 400-MHz range. Providing total premise protection from wall to wall and floor to ceiling, the system will detect any motion in an area of up to 3500 square feet. Sustained human movement for four seconds or more within the protected area will energize the alarm relay contacts, indicating a definite alarm condition.

The on-off switch circuit is impedance controlled and either shorting or cutting the cable between the shunt switch and the unit will result in an alarm. This feature allows use of the on-off switch wiring as a protective circuit by simply installing window foil, magnetic and vibration contacts, floor mats, etc. in series with the shunt switch.

Movement caused by an intruder within a 20- to 30-foot radius of the sensor causes the first alarm stage of the switch to trigger within seconds. If no further movement occurs, the switch will reset itself after a predetermined time. If, however, the intruder makes additional movements in the covered area, a second alarm stage will be triggered, indicating a definite alarm condition. This alarm may be maintained from a few seconds up to several minutes, as selected by an adjustment.

The "Space Switch" may be powered either from 110v AC or 12v DC, and because of the small size, it is easily camouflaged, while the interconnection design permits a multiple- or single-unit alarm system, either as a stand alone or as part of a larger supervisory system. Standby power supplies are offered, too.

Fig. 8-27. Artronix Model 7100 "Space Switch" microwave movement detector.

Fig. 8-28. Artronix Model 6600 with remote sensor.

Other models are available with varying sensitivity ranges, and one (Model 6600) features a dual sensor system which can be used with one or two remote sensors (Fig. 8-28). Problems will occur with remote sensors if the cables between the main unit and the sensors are carelessly laid out or hanging loose. To avoid this problem the sensor cables have to be completely stress relieved and be completely stationary. Normally, movement of the cable cannot be picked up by the sensor, but it creates enough electrostatic noise in the cable itself to trigger the main unit.

BALLISTICS CONTROL CORP.

This company specializes in some radical and unique systems that are worth consideration by anybody interested in protection. A typical example of one of the unusual applications is the system used for boat protection (Fig. 8-29). As you may know, boats are easy prey for burglars, as they are often left untended at their moorings, where they are readily

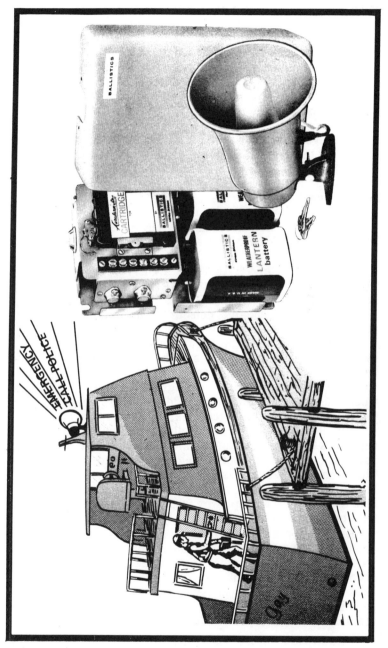

Fig. 8-29. Ballistics Control "Auralarm" Model S4 intruder alarm.

accessible to anybody with a rowboat. On board, there is usually an array of sophisticated and specialized communications equipment and assorted valuables that the owner feels might be safe. Even boats tied at marinas are not always safe, although the marina might provide a guard. Should the area be large enough, even a guard would be hard put to keep a watchful eye over all the boats and persons entering from the land side as well as the sea.

Ballistics offers a protective system that can be triggered by any illegal entry, for only the proper owner has a key that will defeat the system. Should such an unwarranted intrusion occur, the system plays a pre-recorded tape into an amplifier and through a "loud-hailer" atop the cabin. The wording can be your own, but either of the following is typical.

"THERE IS AN INTRUDER ABOARD THIS YACHT. PLEASE SUMMON POLICE AT ONCE!"

Or, if you prefer, "THERE IS AN INTRUDER ABOARD THE YACHT "NANCY GAY," BERTH NO. 78 SOUTH MARINA. PLEASE CALL POLICE AT ONCE."
The message is repeated constantly until the machine is properly deactivated by the owner.

Another version of the Auralarm system is one triggered by any fire-detection system, and the pre-recorded cartridge not only verbally informs residents or other building occupants of the presence of a conflagration, but it actually tells where the fire is located and provides additional safety advice, telling people to use emergency exits and avoid the elevators!

Finally, consider the bank teller faced with a holdup. He depresses the alarm button, summoning help. The next thing you know, the bank robber is under control and in the lockup. This scene has been repeated so often that any robber worth his salt knows that such an alarm button exists, and usually, he'll tell the teller to step away from the button even before he tells him to raise his hands!

Bank robbers have become far less flamboyant lately, preferring to work directly with a bank officer, away from the tellers' cages. Unfortunately, these officers don't usually have access to the alarm buttons; they only have access to the bank's vaults and the money. Ballistics offers a pocket-portable remote radio control that can be pressed to activate the alarm, whether you're near it or not.

And if you're of a mind to install such equipment, you'll find a goodly assortment of attractive and useful accessories, including fire sensors, step-on mats, bells, key locks, magnetic switches, and a couple of unique items that especially aroused our interest. One is a lift-off mat that can be placed under any object, such as a typewriter, television set, or what-have-you. Once the alarm system is activated, lifting a valuable item off the switch causes the alarm to sound. Another item, the money clip, is designed to protect a cash register and sound an alarm if a bill is removed from the register drawer by an unauthorized person.

The DC8D (Fig. 8-30) is a silent, automatic, dialing system that works in conjunction with the existing telephone system, either directly connected or channeled through the phone company's KS20008 alarm coupler. The unit dials direct and is capable of dialing several different phone numbers, transmitting messages to summon help, or to transmit information such as technical conditions or emergencies to interested parties. It repeats the message two or three times as each number answers. If a number dialed is busy, or fails to answer, it automatically calls the next number. This insures instant transmission of urgent messages. DC8D is a dual unit and can be programmed to handle many types of emergencies, such as holdups and fire, boiler and air-conditioning failure, freezer failure and telemetry information. Fig. 8-31 is a block diagram of the DC8D and Fig. 8-32 is a single-channel dialer, Model DC9A.

A telephone line supervision monitor (Model DC8S, Fig. 8-33), is available to monitor the telephone line to insure its

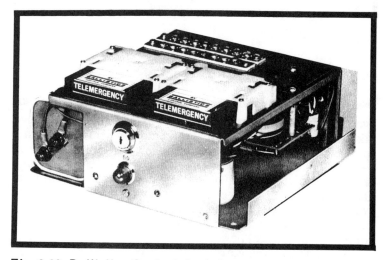

Fig. 8-30. Ballistics Control dual-channel telephone dialer, Model DC8D.

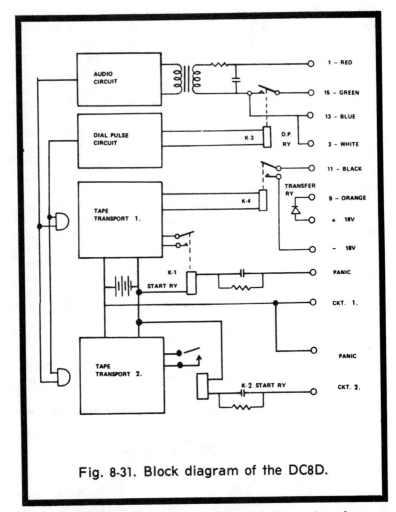

Fig. 8-31. Block diagram of the DC8D.

availability for alarm transmissions. Should any interference take place, the unit will provide contact closure or contact opening (depending on your choice) for you to utilize as you desire. For instance, you can switch over to a secondary and differently routed telephone line; you can activate the local alarm system, or you can construct a separate warning system. The unit takes into account momentary conditions, such as are likely to occur, for instance, when the telephone company switches power supplies. The unit is self-supervising; i.e., the alarm condition occurs should the battery fall below 4.5 volts, plus or minus 0.1 volt, to further insure complete dependability.

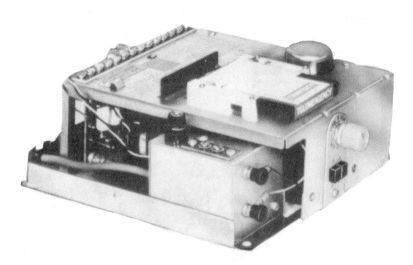

Fig. 8-32. Single-channel telephone dialer, Ballistics Control, DC9A.

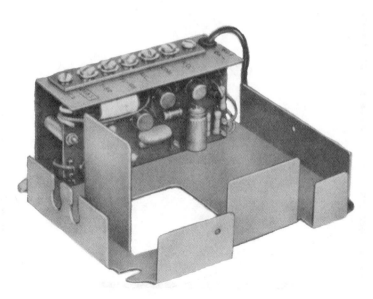

Fig. 8-33. Ballistics Control Model DC8S line supervision monitor.

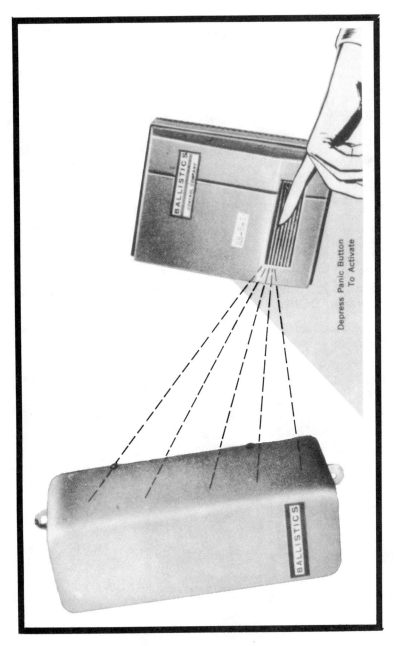

Fig. 8-34. Ballistics Control's moving "panic button," a remote control unit designed to trigger a central alarm which is activated by the receiver.

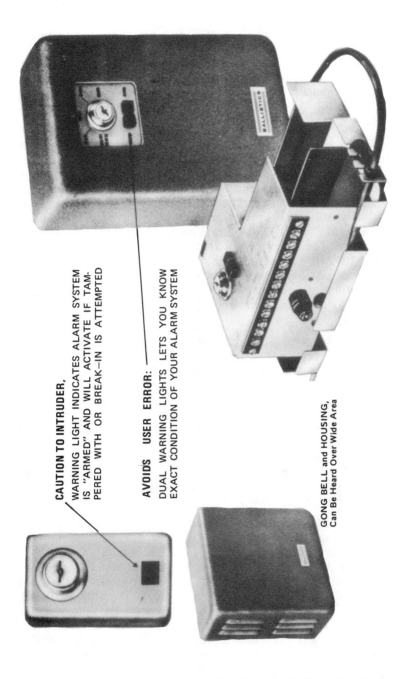

CAUTION TO INTRUDER, WARNING LIGHT INDICATES ALARM SYSTEM IS "ARMED" AND WILL ACTIVATE IF TAMPERED WITH OR BREAK–IN IS ATTEMPTED

AVOIDS USER ERROR: DUAL WARNING LIGHTS LETS YOU KNOW EXACT CONDITION OF YOUR ALARM SYSTEM

GONG BELL and HOUSING, Can Be Heard Over Wide Area

Fig. 8-35. Components used in the Ballistics Control "Bellemergency" system.

The radio control (Fig. 8-34) consists of two basic parts: the transmitter which sends out a coded signal, and the receiver which activates. Two types of transmitters are available for operation of the receiver; a wired-in transmitter for permanent installation and a portable, self-contained transmitter. All units employ completely transistorized circuits.

The portable transmitter is completely self-contained. A clip is provided for fastening it to the user, or it can be carried on the person. No field adjustments are required. The operating distance is from 60 feet to 200 feet depending on local conditions. The radio signal sent out by the transmitter is crystal controlled for operation within the frequency band 26.97 to 27.27 MHz. This band is designated by the FCC for this purpose. The transmitters are design certified as complying with FCC rules: Part 15—Incidental and Restricted Radiation Devices. No license is required. So that neighboring installations will not interfere with each other, the radio signal is coded by a pulsed audio frequency which modulates the radio signal.

The receiver should respond to the transmitter in all directions. If greater range or more equal distance in several directions is desired, try various other locations for the receiver antenna. Extend the antenna toward each wall and corner of the premises, trying the performance in each location. Under particularly adverse conditions, such as might exist with metal lathe in a plastered ceiling or with metal-foil vapor barrier on the walls, it may be desirable to lengthen the antenna. Add enough wire to run the antenna to the wall and down the wall almost to the floor. In extremely adverse cases it may be necessary to run the antenna through the wall and down the outside wall.

The "Bellemergency" (Fig. 8-35) is a sophisticated alarm system for apartments, homes, offices, etc. It aprises you of the safety of your premises by means of a dual warning light system. An inside as well as an outside warning light signals whether the system is on, off, or violated. All controls are completely tamper proof. The user error is eliminated completely. The dual warning light system allows "late-home-comers" to enter without disturbing the rest of the family and neighbors, and yet lets everyone enjoy the safety of complete protection at all times. Upon activation an exceptionally powerful gong bell sounds the alarm to summon help over a wide area. The gong bell is housed in a cabinet for inside or outside installation.

Fig. 8-36. This sampling is typical of the styling available in Bourns systems.

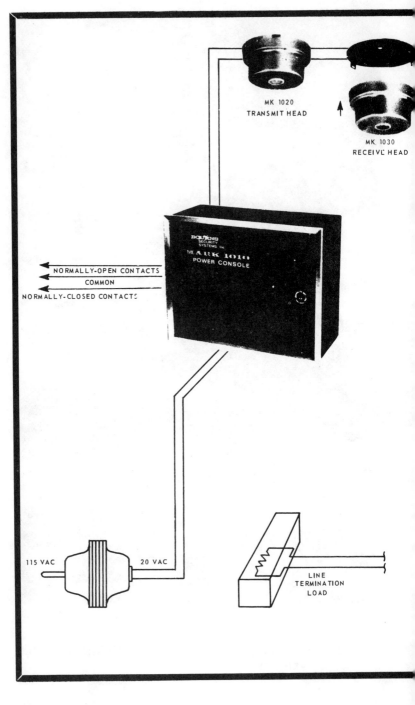

MK 1020
TRANSMIT HEAD

MK 1030
RECEIVE HEAD

BOURNS
SECURITY
SYSTEMS Inc
MARK 1010
POWER CONSOLE

NORMALLY-OPEN CONTACTS
COMMON
NORMALLY-CLOSED CONTACTS

115 VAC   20 VAC

LINE
TERMINATION
LOAD

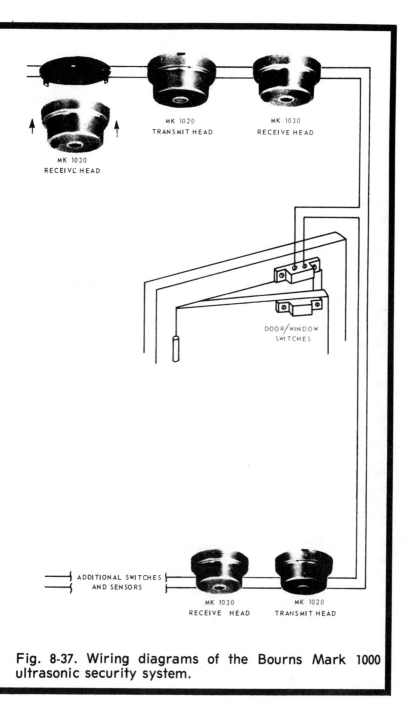

MK 1030
RECEIVE HEAD

MK 1020
TRANSMIT HEAD

MK 1030
RECEIVE HEAD

DOOR/WINDOW
SWITCHES

ADDITIONAL SWITCHES
AND SENSORS

MK 1030
RECEIVE HEAD

MK 1020
TRANSMIT HEAD

Fig. 8-37. Wiring diagrams of the Bourns Mark 1000 ultrasonic security system.

User control of the system is provided by an inside control unit and an outside surface mounted shunt lock. Both units operate in conjunction with each other, making it possible to control the system with the proper key from the inside as well as from the outside. The warning light shows the on or off condition, both outside and inside, eliminating the guesswork where this system is armed or off. The "Bellemergency" is powered primarily by the 115-volt house current and has battery standby in the event that the intruder has cut power lines before breaking into the protected area.

The "Bellemergency" has provisions to hook up to the "Telemergency" automatic dialing system. It can also accommodate a fire detection system which will trigger the gong bell as well as telephone your local fire department.

BOURNS SECURITY SYSTEMS, INC.

The first thing that strikes you about the Bourns equipment is the high styled appearance (Fig. 8-36). It's good looking enough to find a place on a nearby bookshelf, since most units look like classy stereo components. It's a complete ultrasonic home protection system. And there are some pretty clever accessories that go along with it.

For one thing, the system is ultrasonic, which means it detects the movement of a would-be thief. But that isn't all. Door switches provide an extra measure of protection. But let's look at what happens to the poor soul who thinks he's got an easy "hit" on a home protected with the Bourns Equipment:

First of all, a bell alarm sounds. Then a series of floodlights come on to really throw him into panic. He can't shut the system off, as this takes a special key. If he can find any wiring to cut, cutting it doesn't change a thing. All he can do is sit down and wait for the man with the handcuffs.

Fig. 8-37 illustrates a Bourns Mark 1000 installation. The power console (with five hours nominal standby power) is completely tamper-proof. A protective loop circuit alarm activates if the loop is shorted, cut, or if any head is removed. A monitor switch on the power console enables daytime supervision of the protective loop without activating the alarm system. If any head is tampered with or removed during the day, a warning signal is activated at the power console. The system incorporates foolproof, state-of-the-art phase enhancement modulation, a step beyond the Doppler era.

A single 2-conductor loop line cord connects all transmit and receive heads to the power console. Heads can be mounted on conventional outlet boxes or on any flat surface. Swivel mounts are available for directing beam patterns. An individual sensitivity adjustment in each receive head permits quick compensation for room acoustics, and each receive head has an individual trigger lamp for range (sensitivity) adjustment.

All transmit and receive heads are tuned and matched at the factory. No on-site tuning is required. The self-compensating circuit automatically adjusts the system to accommodate any number of heads (up to 40), eliminating delicate, time-consuming balancing.

The Bourns Model A-4 system (Fig. 8-38) turns on a lamp, room lights, or a high-intensity floodlight, and an accessory bell or siren will sound 10 to 20 seconds after the light comes on. The system offers three different frequency channels to prevent the interaction of units used in the same area.

The ACA-150 (Fig. 8-39) appears to be a bookcase speaker cabinet, but it conceals an ultrasonic detection unit and alarm bell which projects a silent, invisible high-frequency beam that effectively "blankets" a given area. The basic enclosure requires no installation; merely connect the ACA-150 to a convenient 110-volt AC outlet. Anyone interrupting its protective beam initiates the alarm system which alerts you and-or frightens away the intruder! The auxiliary protective circuit may be converted to remote "panic" switches, fire sensor, window and door switches, or other separate contact

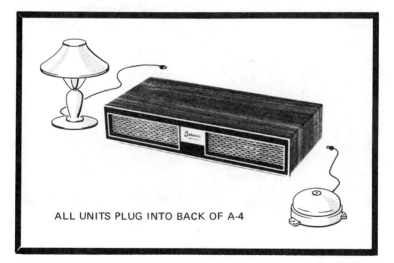

ALL UNITS PLUG INTO BACK OF A-4

Fig. 8-38. The Bourns A-4 intrusion alarm system will work with a variety of accessory components.

Fig. 8-39. Bourns Model ACA-150 senses the presence of an intruder from a conspicuous location.

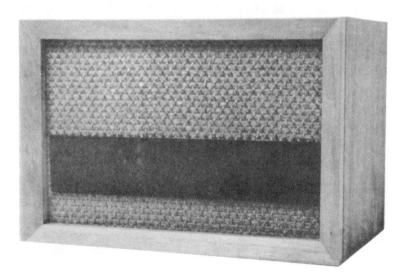

Fig. 8-40. Pictures of an intruder are snapped by the Bourns 700MA system.

devices. This is a closed loop circuit—cutting or opening the circuit activates the alarm.

The 700MA system (Fig. 8-40) also looks like a speaker cabinet but it conceals a sensitive intruder detection system, camera and power package. The invisible high-frequency (ultrasonic) beam effectively "blankets" a given area and operates the camera when the beam is interrupted. The system is easily prepared for operation. It takes pictures at the rate of two per second and can record 2,000 frames before reloading. The camera uses trouble-free film magazines designed to permit safe, easy reloading by nontechnical personnel.

Bourns also has a special marine intrusion alarm (Fig. 8-41) which also uses an ultrasonic beam. It's small, has an anodized case, and fits inconspicuously out of the way, waiting for somebody without permission to dare to board your boat. When he does, it can sound bells, alarms, boat horns, etc. With appropriate sensors, it will detect excessive heat or fire, the presence of water intake due to leaks, water over the cabin sole, in the engine compartment, etc. This fully solid-state unit is fungus treated, too.

Bourns also offers an automatic telephone dialer to automatically transmit emergency messages over the subscriber's regular telephone line. The 600 DI (Fig. 8-42) utilizes a 4-track magazine with two channels—fire and police. These two separate open-circuit inputs can be connected directly to any open-circuit sensor. The tape can be programmed with up to four messages per channel. It stops at the end of the alarm sequence and resets itself automatically. Line seizure is an important feature in this system. It automatically switches the police message to the fire message should burglary and fire occur simultaneously. The fire message always takes priority.

The 600 DI is operated on 110v AC with a 12v standby battery in case of power failure. Low voltage output is provided for an alarm bell, telephone coupler, or warning lights. There are two lights to indicate if AC power or the battery is in operation. The automatic telephone dialing circuit is fully transistorized with heavy-duty screw terminals for various triggering signals. The output terminals supply 600-ohm line impedance power and pulsing-audio data for the telephone company interphase equipment. There are manual controls for setting, resetting and testing. When the control dial is set at the test position, the messages can be monitored through a speaker provided with each unit.

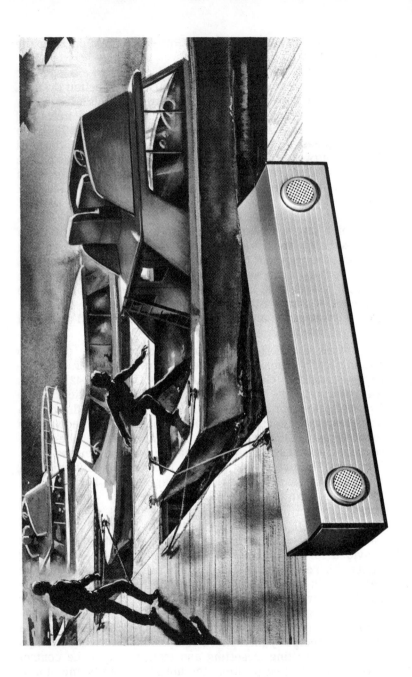

Fig. 8-41. The Bourns Model MA-2 intrusion alarm is designed for marine craft.

The 500EK security camera system (Fig. 8-43) is suited for economy installations such as liquor, drug and grocery stores. This motor-driven camera can be activated on command by a Bourns ultrasonic alarm, a holdup button, treadle, photocell, money clip switch, or similar device to record suspicious or criminal occurrences. It takes pictures at the rate of two per second and can record 2,000 frames before reloading. The system uses trouble-free precision built magazines designed to permit safe, easy reloading by non-technical personnel without danger of film spoilage.

Fig. 8-42. Bourns Model 600 DI automatic telephone dialer.

Fig. 8-43. Model 500 EK security camera system by Bourns
Security Systems.

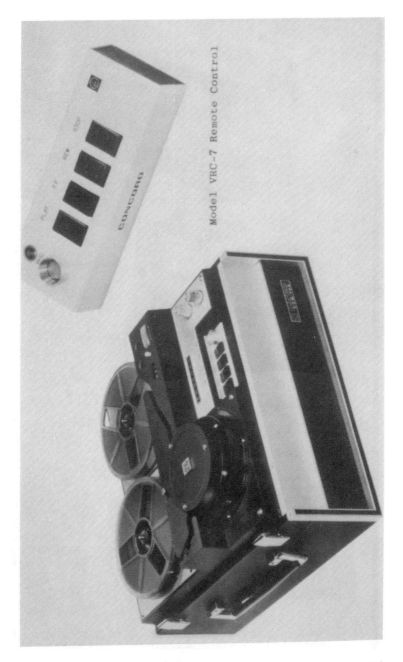

Fig. 8-44. Concord Model VTR700 video tape recorder and VRC-7 remote control unit.

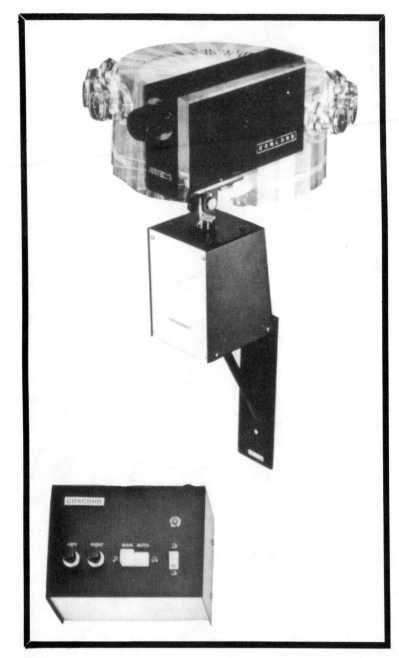

Fig. 8-45. Concord Model VPM-2 camera panning
mechanism with remote control.

How would you like to have a moving picture of the crook that enters and robs your store? Wouldn't that be a nice present for the local police? The Concord intrusion protection system consists of a complete videotape recorder (Fig. 8-44) that sits and waits, then can be activated automatically when a door or window is opened. It makes an ideal system, for the apprehended thief would have to do some pretty fancy side stepping to explain his innocence when you have a video tape of the whole show! It's evidence that's rather hard to refute, isn't it?

Of course, there's always the possibility that a crime can occur during a company's normal business hours. Bank holdups are quite different from bank robberies, in that the stick-up man enters the bank along with the regular customers, maybe even waits in line at a teller's cage before he pulls a gun and makes his robbery. The other recourse is to

Fig. 8-46. This 19-inch monitor can be used to play back video tapes.

chance entering after hours—much more difficult. So how do you get around the problem of video-taping a crook when anybody can walk through the doors?

Concord does it with a time-lapse system, which exposes another piece of video tape in time sequences of one to four frames per second. Add to this a feature (Fig. 8-45) which allows the camera to pan up to 340 degrees and azimuth sweep an arc of 90 degrees, and you can pretty well cover a premises on a 24-hour a day basis. They also supply tapes that will operate in this fashion for up to 48 hours. If there has been no untoward incident in this time, simply rewind, erase, and reuse the tape! The monitor in Fig. 8-46 or any TV receiver can be used to play back video tapes.

DETEX CORPORATION

Anybody who has worked in an urban location is sure to recognize the Detex Watchclock System. The system consists of a portable clock containing a paper recording chart in the form of a dial or tape. The clock is carried by the watchman on his rounds. Throughout the premises there are recording stations located in strategic areas. At each station the guard stops and records his visit on the chart by inserting the station key in the clock.

Now the Detex Corporation has supplemented the foot patrol with a series of electronic surveillance devices in-

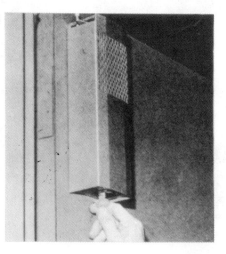

Fig. 8-47. A Detex exit alarm allows authorized personnel to pass.

cluding remote indicating panels, exit alarms and emergency door alarms. Due to this firm's know-how capability, you would do well to send for its booklet, Property Protection Manual.

It is simple to equip a sensitive exit with a Detex exit control lock. The door is always open for emergency "panic" use; however, if it is opened by unauthorized personnel—either for an emergency or, for example, during a robbery—a loud alarm immediately summons security personnel. The alarm is rarely sounded, though, since the panic bar plate carries a warning that states, "Emergency Exit Only. Push here; alarm will sound."

In normal use, personnel carrying a proper key can open the door without sounding the alarm and let it open for as long as desired. When the door is relocked, the warning system is rearmed.

Another method of tightening security at most doorways is to use a Detex exit alarm (Fig. 8-47). This equipment assures maximum "on-the-spot" protection in a wide range of applications at low cost. It can be used independently or linked with existing systems. Only authorized personnel with special keys can get by the exit alarm. Nonauthorized use triggers a loud, continuous blast by horns built right into the unit. The warning continues to sound until the alarm circuit is reset.

The exit alarm is compact, rugged, tamper-proof, and self-contained. Power is provided by alkaline cells. It may be

Fig. 8-48. Detex remote indicating panel monitors a number of doors from one location.

Fig. 8-49. Remote panel for monitoring a single door.

mounted on either the door or the doorframe in either a horizontal or vertical position. It may be used with single or double doors, both inswinging and outswinging. Through use of a single, replaceable control cylinder, it is ideal for use with master key systems. It is especially suitable for doors with existing ordinary panic hardware.

Remote indicating panels (Fig. 8-48) provide a means of monitoring several doors from one location. Used in conjunction with Detex exit control locks or exit alarms, one guard can keep track of 10, 20, 30 or more doors. Whenever a protected door is used, the unit goes into action. A buzzer sounds and the appropriate signal flashes on. (This is in addition to the local alarm which sounds at the door itself.) Panels may also be used to monitor a number of other functions besides door use; water flow alarms, gate operators, boilers, production and maintenance equipment.

Where only one door opening is to be protected with a remote alarm, the RIP-101 (Fig. 8-49) is a good, economical choice. It operates on a single, low-voltage circuit and may also be used as a supplementary increased sound warning unit.

ELECTRONIC LOCATOR CORP.

Where do you get the necessary accessories that go with any good installation? Electronic Locator Corp. is a good source. Control instruments are available, prewired, and ready for connection to a system consisting of an alarm, a battery or power source, and a protective circuit (Fig. 8-50). Finished boxes, drilled and tapped to accommodate these circuits, are also available.

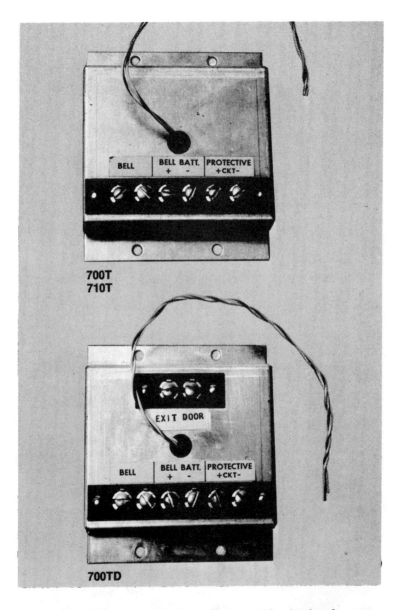

Fig. 8-50. These control units are typical of many available from Electronic Locator Corp. The 700T is a closed-circuit control for local alarms. By adding the relay (710T) supplied, the same control can be used to sound 110v sirens. The 700TD is the same as the 700T with a silent delayed entry on an exit door.

Fig. 8-51. Electronic Locator Corp. offers a variety of bells and sirens, plus enclosures with tamperproof switches.

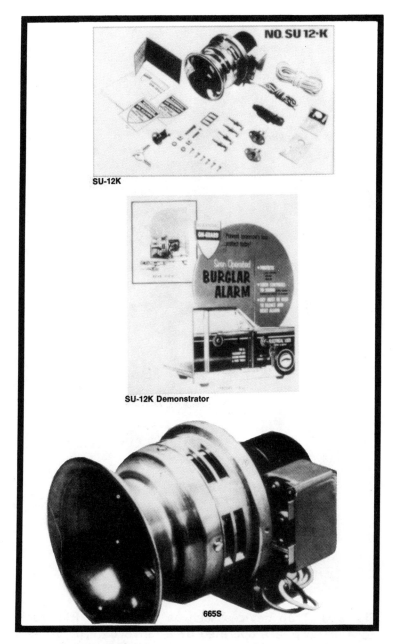

SU-12K

SU-12K Demonstrator

665S

Fig. 8-52. Complete vehicle alarm system available from Electronic Locator Corp. The police-type siren (665S) sounds when any door, hood or trunk is opened.

Fig. 8-53. Trap devices such as these from Electronic Locator Corp. are operated by a lanyard. Type 674 is a closed-circuit noninsulated device, 675 is a closed-circuit insulated type, and 676 is an open-circuit insulated pull trap.

Bells and sirens (Fig. 8-51) of several types are offered, plus weatherproof housings for these units. There's also an automatic telephone dialing mechanism, an assortment of smoke and heat detectors, and complete systems for several applications, including vehicle alarms (Fig. 8-52). There is a wide assortment of electric key locks to arm and de-arm the entire system.

The traps in Fig. 8-53 (sophisticated clothespin and celluloid strip devices!) are simply two ball contacts separated by a tongue. The tongue is attached to a lanyard which goes to a door or window. The length of the lanyard determines the degree to which a door or window is to be opened. Should a door or window be moved further than that, the lanyard will extract the tongue, close the circuit, and sound the alarm.

Window slides (Fig. 8-54) are mounted on sliding windows. When the window is raised, the arm comes out and completes the alarm circuit. Where windows or doors swing outward, B-spring contacts are used to close the circuit.

This is the place to get the foil (Fig. 8-55) you need for protecting glass windows, and the foil contactors which rest a spring whisker on the foil. And yes, they have the adhesive as well. Other items include switch mats (Fig. 8-56), contacts (8-57) and reed magnetic contact switches (Fig. 8-58).

HOLMES ELECTRIC PROTECTIVE COMPANY

Whether your domicile is a rented apartment or a privately owned home, the Holmes system of total protection is worth investigating. It's a wired system, basically, and one that provides a multitude of services. Sensors placed at strategic places, are wired to a central office (Figs. 8-59 through 8-65). When you lock up for the night, you operate your key in the switch to notify the central office. A return signal assures you that your lockup has been recorded at the central office and that they are on the alert. Should a forced entry occur, an alerting light comes on, indicating to the office that an intrusion has occurred. Duplicate keys to your domicile are removed from a file and a car with armed, well-trained guards is dispatched immediately to your premises. It's the guards that are truly the key to the system, for they are trained in the legalities as well as the techniques and know how to apprehend a would-be criminal and to do it safely, surely and with dispatch.

As an added safety device, a signal button is provided, should you overhear an entry in progress that has not as yet

119

been culminated. Pressing this silent switch sends the same warning alert to the office, getting the guards there in a hurry. These buttons can also be used for summoning aid when other means of communication, such as your telephone, aren't functioning. And that's the beginning.

Holmes also serves major business firms and stores as well. They offer such accessories as retractable steel guard doors (Figs. 8-66 and 8-67), fire sensors, and have recently gone into the business of photographic detection also. Silent cameras can be installed in your place of business to actually photograph would-be burglars in the act of the crime they are about to commit. These stop-action cameras not only take clear, sharp photos, but prints are immediately rushed to you and the local police to serve as an aid in apprehending a criminal after the fact (Fig. 8-68).

The problem seems to be that small protections can lull us into a false sense of security. The home owner feels that his suburban residence is so peaceful and quiet that he will hear an interloper and waken in time to phone the police. But consider for a moment that the smart burglar will cut the telephone wires before he enters your home. When a problem takes place, you pick up the phone and hear nothing at all—no dial tone, no noise, just absolute silence—your phone is dead.

In urban areas, apartment houses are often protected by a doorman and perhaps an elevator operator. Yet a smart thief, well dressed, can enter as a guest and go unquestioned to any apartment in the building. Should he be questioned, he needs only to say that he made a mistake and entered the wrong apartment house. He cannot be arrested, for he has committed no crime!

The Holmes system connects your home to the central office by means of underground cables. There is a small installation cost and then a regular monthly fee for the duration of the time the service is used. Along with the installation a decal is applied to the front door to announce the fact that the premises are protected by the Company.

Obviously, to gain maximum benefit from a system such as this, you must be located in an area that is served by the Company. There would be little or no value in having such an installation where it would take the protection officers too long a time to arrive at your premises, not to mention the cost of wiring. However, this firm manufactures all of the components it sells or leases, thereby offering many home owners and businessmen some of the benefits of Holmes protection even though the establishment to be protected is beyond the normal range of the Company's facilities.

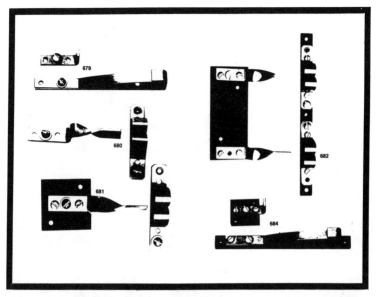

Fig. 8-54. Window slides (679 and 684) and B springs (680, 681, 682) are useful in protecting doors and windows.

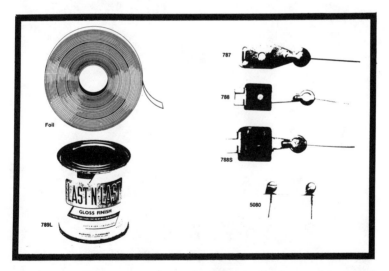

Fig. 8-55. Foil protection supplies include noninsulated spring whisker (787), an insulated spring whisker (788), an insulated short spring whisker (788S), insulated glue block with an adhesive designed to mount on glass (5080), foil, and foil adhesive.

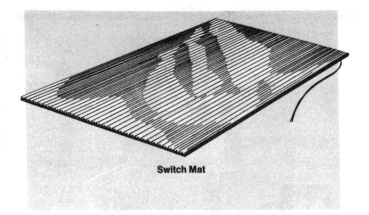

Switch Mat

Fig. 8-56. Switch mats are available in various sizes, sealed and unsealed, from Electronic Locator Corp.

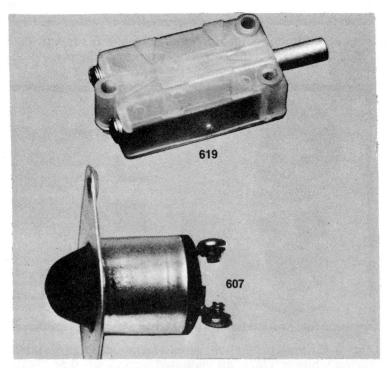

619

607

Fig. 8-57. Contact assemblies; an all-weather tamper-proof switch (619) and a flush-mount "button" type which is available in open- and closed-circuit configurations.

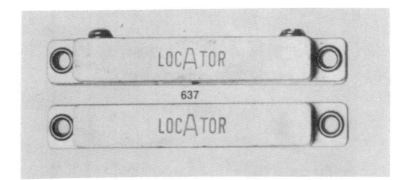

Fig. 8-58. Reed magnetic contact switches.

Fig. 8-59. A Holmes central office servicing thousands of subscribers in a metropolitan area.

Fig. 8-60. Over 5,000 lines to subscribers terminate at this office, the largest of its kind in the world. At this point, they are connected to the Holmes switchboard serving each subscriber.

Fig. 8-61. Huge storage batteries supply direct current to operate the Holmes systems. Two sets of batteries, plus auxiliary standby equipment, provide a continuous, unfailing source of supply, even though the public utility electric supply might fail.

Fig. 8-62. From these galvanometers, the Holmes operator knows every minute of the day and night of any unusual conditions with the protective system.

Fig. 8-63. A set of keys for each subscriber is maintained in a locked file at the Holmes Service Office. These keys are kept in tamperproof envelopes protected by serially numbered lead seals. Identically numbered envelopes containing authorized signatures are filed with the keys. Only the Service Office Manager has access to the locked file containing these keys and signature cards.

Fig. 8-64. During the closed period, two Holmes guards are normally dispatched to answer every alarm. One immediately signals the Central Office that they have entered the premises while the other starts to investigate. On their return, guards make detailed notes on the incident, and a written report is mailed to the customer.

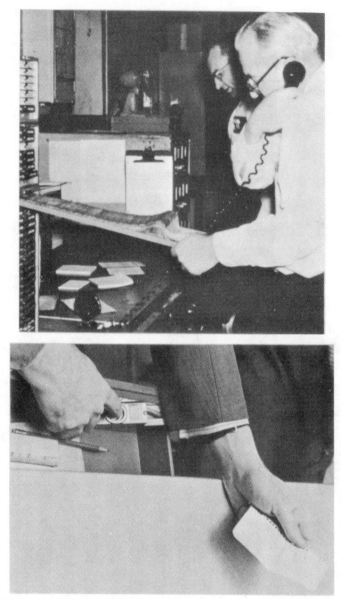

Fig. 8-65. A series of strategically located and concealed Holmes alarm stations permit the alarm of a holdup to be given silently and inconspicuously. The Holmes Central Office springs into instant action on receipt of a holdup alarm. Usually less than a minute elapses before the police are on their way.(This is an actual alarm situation.)

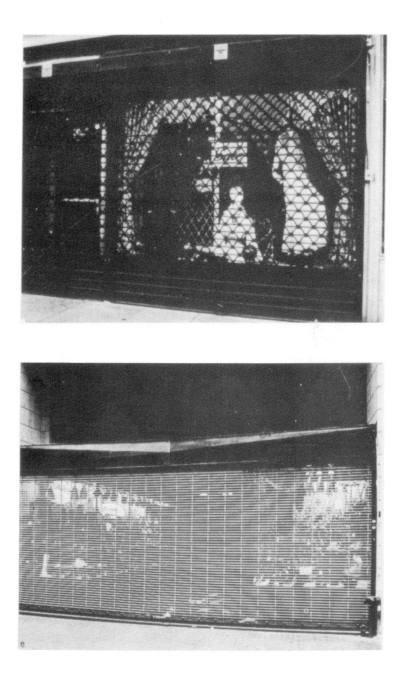

Fig. 8-66. Retractable steel guard doors installed by Holmes Electric.

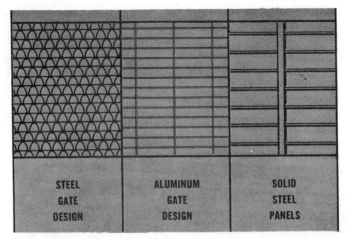

| STEEL GATE DESIGN | ALUMINUM GATE DESIGN | SOLID STEEL PANELS |

Fig. 8-67. Holmes "anti-assault gates" are designed to enhance the exterior of any type of street-level business establishment. Two designs of mesh and a solid panel are available. Each installation is equipped with a vertical canopy of steel which conceals the gate when retracted and also provides a space for store identification.

The Holmes Apartment Intrusion Device (AID) is interesting in its several fail-safe features (Fig. 8-69). Should the mechanism or its wiring be tampered with, an alert signal goes out, summoning help. Should you fail to activate the device, or turn it off, you can still summon assistance by pressing the call button. That's right, even with the unit **off**! How expensive is this service? "Less than a pack of cigarettes a day," according to a Company spokesman.

MULTI-ELMAC'S SECURITY SYSTEM

This is a unique and attractive wireless alarm system, operating in the Citizens Band on frequencies set aside for industrial applications. Basically, the system consists of a radio transmitter and a radio receiver. It's an ideal answer to those problems where wiring is taboo for one reason or another, yet the system stands on its own merit, wired or otherwise.

Several transmitters are available, but basically they are housed in a plastic pocket container with a pushbutton trigger. The transmitter sends out a coded signal that activates the receiver, and this two- or three-signal code eliminates the possibility that a nearby garage door opener will sound your

Fig. 8-68. This sequence of photos was snapped by a Holmes stop-action camera.

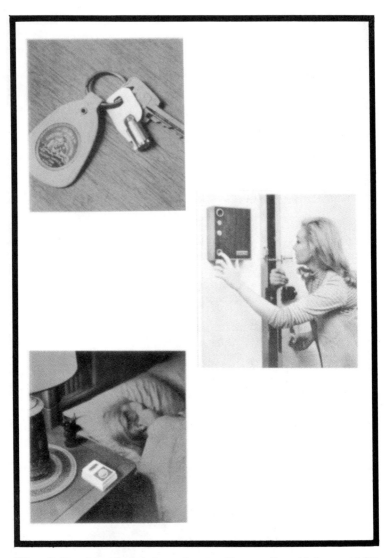

Fig. 8-69. A special key turns it on, the Holmes AID system—the only way it can be turned on and off. The "hot line" alarm can be pressed quickly, silently, and secretly should danger threaten. It is always on—ready to bring armed-guard help—even if the full system is turned off. A remote control can be installed any where—bedroom, kitchen, near the TV. A push of the button causes the Electronic Brain to instantly signal for aid, when the system is turned on.

alarm. The system also meets FCC requirements for constant signal transmission, as there's a duration on-duration off time factor.

The Multi-Elmac Company Models 1604-11, -12, -13, -14 are 2-tone 27-MHz transmitters (Fig. 8-70) that are specifically manufactured for security applications. These transmitters employ a special coding that is the primary distinguishing feature of the entire line of Multi-Elmac security radio controls and prevents accidental operation by any of the Multi-Elmac controls that are used to operate residential garage doors or that are used for industrial and commercial purposes. When used in conjunction with any of the 1600 model series receivers, the 1604 transmitters will provide wireless remote control that can be conveniently and economically used in security and alarm systems without a transmitting license. These transmitters are designed to operate the Multi-Elmac security receivers quickly and reliably when both units are set to the same code. The three-frequency coding used in the 1600 series of controls is composed of a radio frequency (RF) carrier, and audio frequency (AF) subcarrier and a low frequency (LF) second tone. These models are designed specifically to be used in conjunction with security and alarm

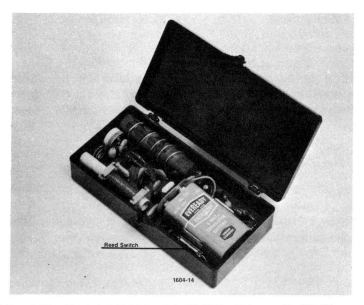

Fig. 8-70. Model 1604-13, -14 27-MHz 2-tone Multi-Elmac security transmitter.

systems, and have operational characteristics which make them easily adaptable to and compatible with the many concepts of property protection.

Model 1604-13 is built for use in closed circuits and the Model 1604-11 is for use in open circuits. Each is housed in a 2¼ x 4½ x 1 inch styrene plastic case or may be enclosed in the system's cabinet. They have no pushbutton, but are furnished with 4-inch wire leads for connection to an external normally closed switch or a closed circuit system. The briefest momentary opening (or closing in the 1604-11 and -12) of the switch or system locks in a timing circuit which causes the transmitter to radiate a signal for 8 to 10 seconds. At the end of this period, the transmitter shuts itself off and does not repeat, nor is there continued battery drain. After approximately 30 seconds, the timing circuit will recharge itself and be ready for another signal transmission, if the switch or circuit is momentarily opened. Another feature of this same circuit is that, if the activating switch is closed and remains closed (or open and remains opened, 1604-11 and -12), the transmitter will radiate the signal for the 8- or 10-second period but will not repeat nor cause battery drain so long as the switch remains closed. When the switch is opened the circuit will, in approximately 30 seconds, recharge itself and, if the switch is again closed, repeat the cycle.

Model 1604-12 has the identical features and operational characteristics of Model 1604-11 except Model 1604-12 is furnished with a normally closed reed switch, instead of wire leads, and is used in conjunction with a holding magnet (not furnished). Movement of the magnet from the transmitter permits the reed switch to close and causes the circuit to emit a signal for the 8- or 10-second period. Moving the magnet back to "set" position permits recharging the circuit. Power for the standard 1604 transmitter is furnished by a self-contained premium 9-volt dry cell battery. Battery power consumption during operation is minimal and a fresh battery will generally last at least a year in normal intermittent service.

On special order, these transmitters can be furnished to operate from an external source of 12 volts direct current (DC). This external power source can be a rechargeable nickel-cadmium battery, an automotive-type storage battery, or a suitably rectified and filtered transformer supply connected to the 115-volt AC power line.

The Model 1604-01 is essentially the same as the -11 and -13, except for the housing (Fig. 8-71).

A fixed transmitter type is also available which provides for sensors other than the pushbutton. This unit can also be mounted away from view, and the only wiring required in this case is the sensor-to-transmitter wiring. The transmitter will function if any open-circuit sensor is closed; therefore, heat or smoke detectors, proximity magnetic switches, reed switches, or simple electrical contacts or miniature microswitches can be used. This system also lends itself to full-time use with a little ingenuity. During daytime, switch from the alarm to a less rambunctious type of signal, and the units make a fine calling device, an excellent adjunct to a sick room, for example.

The Multi-Elmac Company Models 1603-01 through 1603-23 are 2-tone 27-MHz receivers that are specifically manufactured for security applications. These receivers employ a special coding that is the primary distinguishing feature of the entire line of Multi-Elmac security radio controls and prevents accidental operation by any of the Multi-Elmac controls that are used to operate residential garage doors or that are used for industrial and commercial purposes. When used in conjunction with any of the 1600 model series transmitters, these receivers will provide wireless remote control with a "sequence" relay output that can be conveniently and economically used in security and alarm systems.

Upon receipt of a proper signal, a set of relay contacts in the receiver will close, and remain closed until a second signal

Fig. 8-71. Model 1604-01, -10 transmitter by Multi-Elmac.

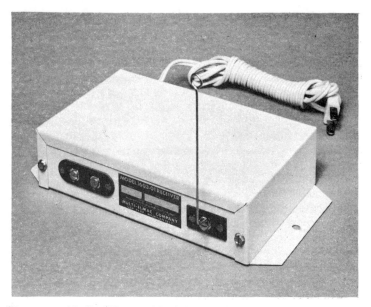

Fig. 8-72. Multi-Elmac Model 1603 Series 27-MHz security receivers.

is received. A double throw relay and proper terminal can be supplied, so that a set of "closed" contacts and a set of "open" contacts are available at each cycle. These contacts, which in the 1603 receiver series are rated at 3 amperes, are connected to the apparatus to be controlled.

These receivers are designed to operate quickly and reliably from only the matching transmitters. They respond to a particular combination of three coding frequencies that are emitted by the proper transmitters. The three frequency code used in this receiver is composed of a radio frequency (RF) carrier, an audio frequency (AF) subcarrier tone and a low frequency (LF) second tone. A time delay feature rejects the signal until the proper combination has been sustained for at least one-half second. Specific values of the standard channel frequencies available are listed in the specifications.

The receivers are built for easy installation. They may be mounted in any position near the apparatus to be controlled, using two screws. The receivers are in compact enclosures and are supplied with detailed installation instructions and one or more matching transmitters. The circuit boards of these receivers may be furnished without the case for mounting directly in the cabinet that is being used to house the primary system.

The 1603 Series receivers require external antennas, although the type, length and placement of this antenna are not especially critical. Generally good results will be obtained with a simple wire antenna approximately 2 to 6 feet long (approximately 0.5 to 2 meters). The longer antenna is useful where greater operating distances are desired while the shorter antenna is a more convenient length to locate in restricted areas. Changing the antenna length does not require receiver readjustments.

The Model 1603-01, -11, -21 receivers are powered by normal 115-volt AC line power and are built to operate over a wide range of environmental conditions. The electric power consumption is small, approximately equal to that of a household electric clock.

The Model 1603-02, -12, -22 receivers are furnished to operate on 12 volts DC. This can be an automotive type storage battery, but generally is connected to the built-in power supply of the equipment with which it is being used. On special order Model 1603-22 can be adapted to other DC voltages.

The Model 1603-03, -13, -23 receivers are furnished to operate on AC power and have a built-in 12-volt trickle charge for standby battery, and automatically switch over to that standby power in the event of main AC power failure.

The relay contact arrangement in the receivers are standard as single pole single throw normally open (SPST-NO) or Form A. On special orders, receivers can be furnished with additional relay contacts with up to two poles and with either Form A (normally open), Form B (normally closed) or Form C (double throw) contact arrangements. Relay contact ratings up to 10 amperes can also be furnished for special applications.

All Multi-Elmac radio controls are accurately pretuned to standard frequencies, are completely tested and are ready for installation and operation. Additional matching transmitters or receivers, if needed at a later date, may be obtained by specifying the model number and frequency code number imprinted on the serial plate.

PYROTRONICS, INC.

The heart of this company's system is a series of detectors (Fig. 8-73) that sense the presence of invisible airborne combustion products. The ionization detector (Figs. 8-75 and 8-76) senses fire in the incipient stage, even overloaded electrical circuits or existence of the elements necessary for spontaneous combustion. There is neither smoke nor flame,

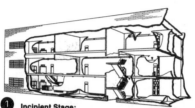

Incipient Stage:

No visible smoke, flame or significant heat is being developed. However, a condition exists (e.g. electric overload) which generates a significant amount of combustion particles. These particles have weight and mass, but are too small in size to be visible to the human eye. These particles behave according to gas laws and quickly rise to the ceiling. This stage usually develops over a long extended period of time, usually minutes or hours.

Pyr-A-Larm Ionization Detectors can respond to the invisible combustion products.

Smoldering Stage:

As the fire condition develops the quantity of combustion particles increase to the poi(n)t where their collective mass becomes visible. This we refer to as "smoke". There is still n(o) flame or significant heat developed.

Pyr-A-Larm Photo-electric Detectors can respond to the visible smoke.

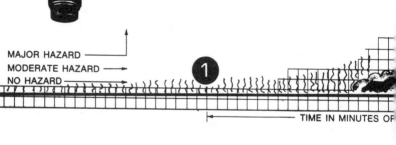

MAJOR HAZARD

MODERATE HAZARD

NO HAZARD

TIME IN MINUTES OF

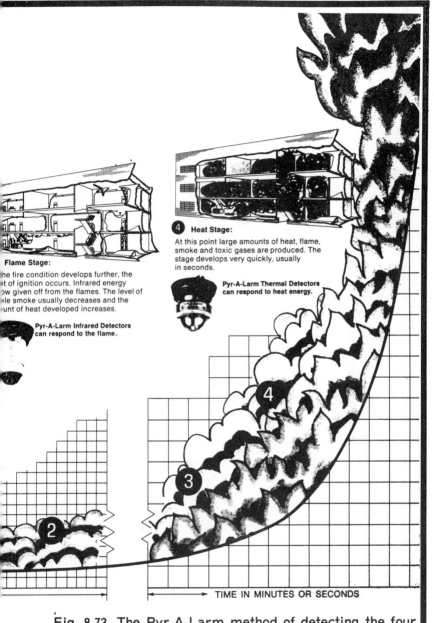

Flame Stage:

he fire condition develops further, the
t of ignition occurs. Infrared energy
ow given off from the flames. The level of
le smoke usually decreases and the
unt of heat developed increases.

**Pyr-A-Larm Infrared Detectors
can respond to the flame.**

④ **Heat Stage:**

At this point large amounts of heat, flame,
smoke and toxic gases are produced. The
stage develops very quickly, usually
in seconds.

**Pyr-A-Larm Thermal Detectors
can respond to heat energy.**

TIME IN MINUTES OR SECONDS

Fig. 8-73. The Pyr-A-Larm method of detecting the four
stages of fire.

1 The Pyr-A-Larm Unit provides power for the system, indicates the zone of the detector that responded and can control equipment, operate vents, extinguisher systems, etc.

2 The Pyr-A-Larm Manual Alarm Station, advanced style, operates on a modified pull-lever principle.

3 The Pyr-A-Larm Trouble Horn calls attention to personnel that trouble has developed on the system.

4 The Pyr-A-Larm Remote Annunciator duplicates signals of the Fire and Zone Indicating Units. All Signals, Fire, Power, Trouble and Zone are indicated visually.

5 The Pyr-A-Larm recessed ceiling fixture makes it possible to recess the Pyr-A-Larm ionization detector into a ceiling.

6 The Pyr-A-Larm Remote Alarm Lamp identifies a concealed detector initiating the alarm.

7 The Pyr-A-Larm Door Holder provides automatic control over fire doors.

8 The Pyr-A-Larm Alarm Bell provides clear signals of a high decibel output on low current input.

9 A Pyr-A-Larm ionization detector mounted in concealed areas provides a system with complete early warning protection.

10 The Pyr-A-Larm Ionization Plug-in Detector reacts to the first stages of fire.

11 The Pyr-A-Larm Air Duct Detector prevents the recirculation of combustion products and smoke in air handling system.

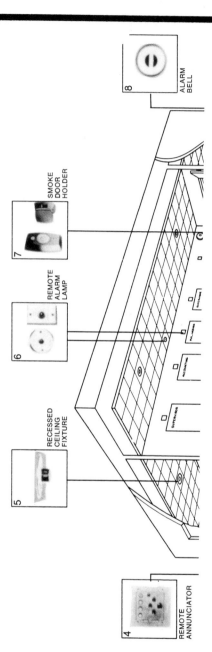

RECESSED CEILING FIXTURE 5

REMOTE ALARM LAMP 6

SMOKE DOOR HOLDER 7

ALARM BELL 8

REMOTE ANNUNCIATOR 4

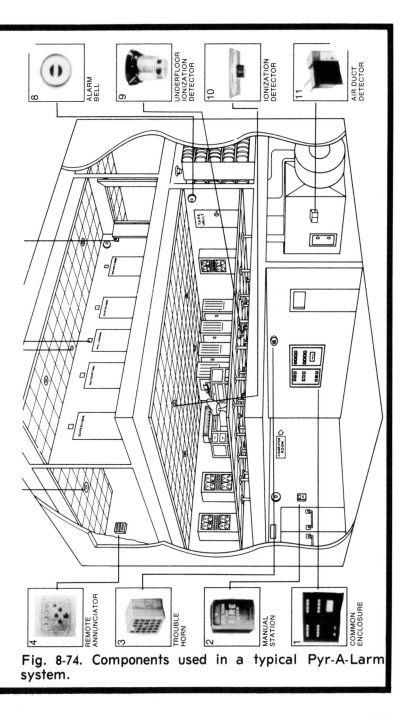

8 ALARM BELL

9 UNDERFLOOR IONIZATION DETECTOR

10 IONIZATION DETECTOR

11 AIR DUCT DETECTOR

4 REMOTE ANNUNCIATOR

3 TROUBLE HORN

2 MANUAL STATION

1 COMMON ENCLOSURE

Fig. 8-74. Components used in a typical Pyr-A-Larm system.

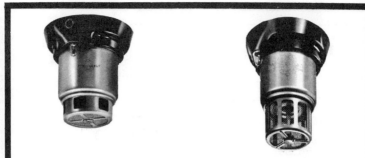

Fig. 8-75. Pyrtronics ionization fire detectors.

Fig. 8-76. Air duct ionization fire detector.

Fig. 8-77. Pyrotronics flame fire detectors.

nor is there elevated temperature at this point, but conditions leading to a fire hazard are present. The ionization detector senses this change in the gaseous condition of the room.

When smoldering commences, smoke is produced, and a photoelectric detector takes over, sensing the presence of visible smoke. When the above condition occurs, it isn't long before flame is present, and an infrared detector (Fig. 8-77), available from this company, responds to flame. Finally, the conflagration bursts forth, and another element senses the increased temperature (Fig. 8-78).

In addition to these basic sensors, this company manufacturers some unique products, including a built-in lamp which goes on when a detector has been triggered, thereby indicating which detector (and therefore in what location) the problem exists. Another unique product is a smoke door holder (Fig. 8-80), which holds a fire door open with an electromagnetic latch. When smoke is detected, the magnet releases, allowing the door to close. Frankly, the nearest thing we've seen to this until now is a door that is held open by a fusible link that melts under heat and releases a weight which closes the door.

The Pyrotronic complete fire-protective system has found wide application in such institutions as government, computer, hospitals, schools, hotels, libraries, museums, retail stores and many residences. Fig. 8-74 illustrates a typical Pyr-A-Larm system installed in a multi-story structure. A computer installation is shown in Fig. 8-79.

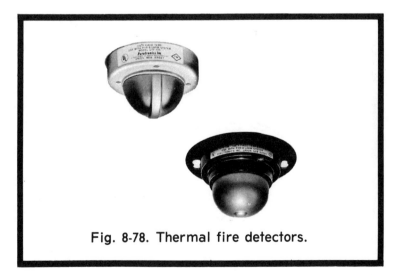

Fig. 8-78. Thermal fire detectors.

PYR-A-LARM®

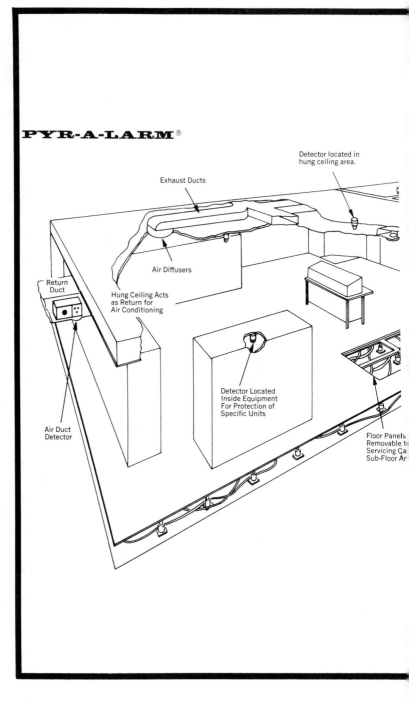

Detector located in hung ceiling area.

Exhaust Ducts

Air Diffusers

Return Duct

Hung Ceiling Acts as Return for Air Conditioning

Detector Located Inside Equipment For Protection of Specific Units

Air Duct Detector

Floor Panels Removable t Servicing Ca Sub-Floor Ar

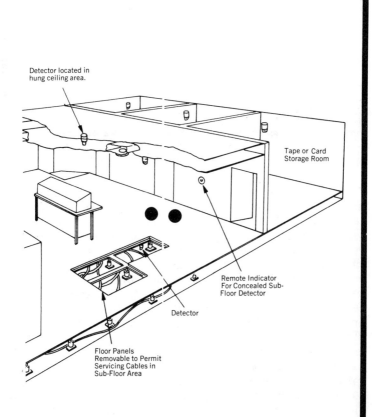

Detector located in
hung ceiling area.

Tape or Card
Storage Room

Remote Indicator
For Concealed Sub-
Floor Detector

Detector

Floor Panels
Removable to Permit
Servicing Cables in
Sub-Floor Area

Fig. 8-79. Pyrotronics fire detection check list for a computer installation.

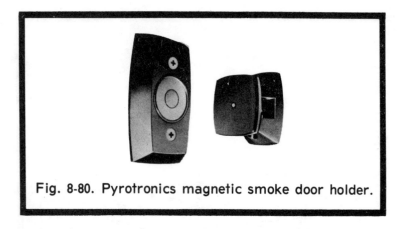

Fig. 8-80. Pyrotronics magnetic smoke door holder.

RADAR DEVICES MANUFACTURING CO.

If you're interested and qualify, this firm will help put you in business. They're tooled up to just that kind of activity, with sales aids, protected franchise areas, everything you need to sell and install Radar Devices systems. They'll gladly show you a breakdown of potential profits, and they offer consultation and advice when needed.

The Radar Sentry System is a microwave type, tailored to fit in any sort of an installation, with the antenna set up remotely from the control unit (Fig. 8-81). Along with the antenna and control unit, you will find an assortment of alarms, including bells, sirens and telephone dialers that you can program yourself. There are assorted inputs, too.

A remote detector, actually an antenna, relays microwaves generated by a very stable oscillator. Within a 5000-square-foot-area floor-to-ceiling, the load is set. Any slight human movement changes this load, which in turn changes the frequency.

Amplified by a series of ultra-stable transistor stages, this change is detected and automatically goes into use to operate the alarm relay. If he hides on the premises all day, waiting to burglarize at night, he is detected the instant he moves because radar waves saturate the protected area, wall-to-wall, floor-to-ceiling.

Each RSA detector radiates microwaves in a circle of approximately 35 feet, and accessories are available to extend coverage up to 15,000 square feet. Any human movement, even the slightest gesture, will set the alarm off. There is no way to beat it. No way to hide from it. No way to escape detection, whether the intruder comes in through the wall, the window or breaks through the ceiling. If he should shut off the power, the alarm will sound. If the intruder even tampers with the unit during the day, it will sound off with a fail-safe alarm. And even during a complete power failure, the unit works constantly as the optional built-in rechargeable storage cell batteries take over. Radar Sentry Alarm can be used with on-location police sirens to frighten off burglars and intruders, or as a silent alarm, with a direct line to police headquarters. Some accessory units appear in Fig. 8-83.

A telephone dialer (Fig. 8-84) connects your Radar Sentry Alarm directly to the police station, the fire house, or your home. It automatically dials the phone and delivers any pre-recorded message for which it is programmed. Fires are reported to the fire department and burglaries to the police. The DT-1000 will not only notify the proper officials, but it will back up the first call by calling you or any other person designated. The Dialtronic can also be programmed to handle two different emergencies, automatically dialing the right people and delivering the correct message in each case.

Radar Sentry Alarm installation is simplicity itself. Anyone capable of installing a door bell or TV antenna can

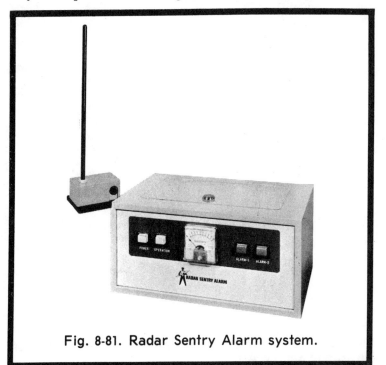

Fig. 8-81. Radar Sentry Alarm system.

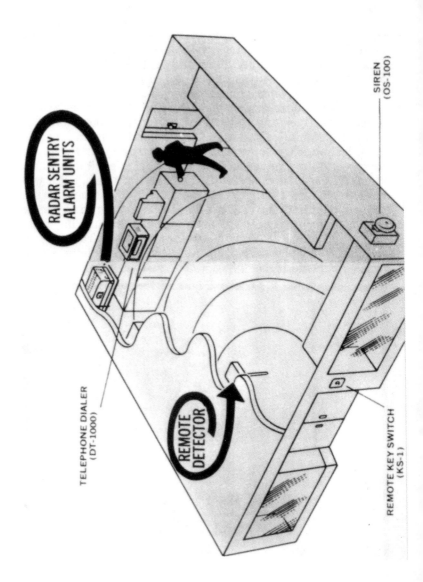

RADAR SENTRY ALARM UNITS

SIREN (OS-100)

TELEPHONE DIALER (DT-1000)

REMOTE DETECTOR

REMOTE KEY SWITCH (KS-1)

Fig. 8-82. Drawing of a typical commercial installation of the Radar Sentry Alarm.

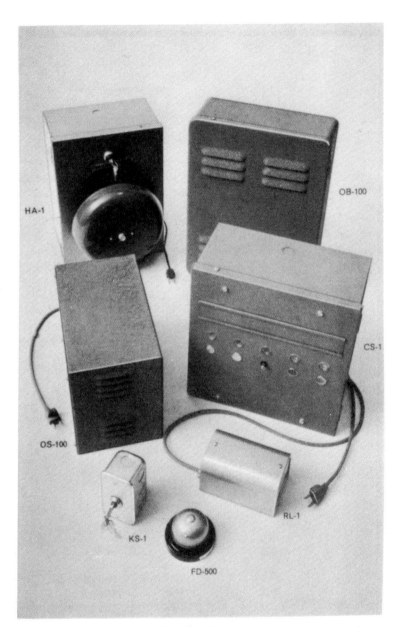

Fig. 8-83. Some Radar Sentry Alarm system accessories; fire sensor (FD-500), remote key switch (KS-1), relay unit (RL-1), outside siren (OS-100), telephone alarm (CS-1), wireless control holdup and prowler alarm (HA-1), and outside alarm and tamper bell (OB-100).

149

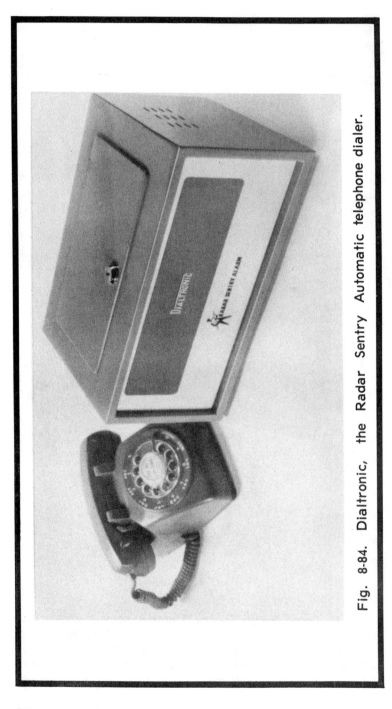

Fig. 8-84. Dialtronic, the Radar Sentry Automatic telephone dialer.

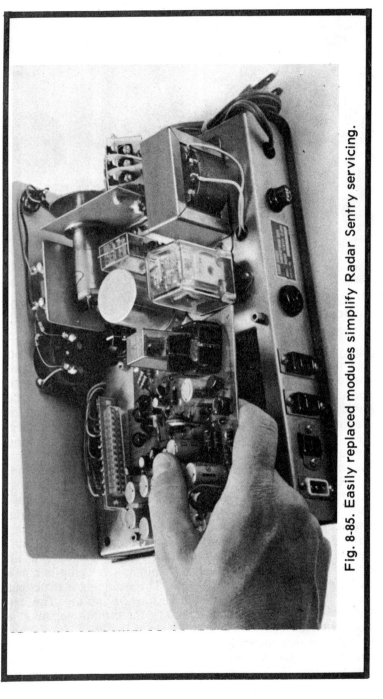

Fig. 8-85. Easily replaced modules simplify Radar Sentry servicing.

151

Fig. 8-86. Wireless prowler alarm control and the alarm device (inset).

easily complete a basic installation in less than an hour. You just find a place for the Radar Sentry Alarm—plug it in, connect accessories, turn it on, and tell your customer how to operate it. Systems with remote detectors and accessories do require some installation, but this is primarily a matter of placing the units physically and connecting them together. You will receive complete easy-to-follow installation and operating instructions with every Radar Sentry Alarm system. Remote units can be moved from location to location.

Radar Sentry Alarms are completely solid-state; therefore, they require a minimum of service. And because they are modular, they can be serviced by anyone—even someone with very limited technical knowledge. The Company recommends that each dealer keep a complete Radar Sentry Alarm in stock. If a customer's unit ever goes out, all he has to do is pull out the defective module and plug in a new module from the spare (Fig. 8-85). The servicing instructions make it easy to spot the defective module rapidly. The bad module is simply sent to the factory for prompt repair at a nominal cost.

The device shown in Fig. 8-86 can be used as a prowler alarm by the homeowner or as a holdup alarm by businessmen. It is used to protect premises while they are

CAN BE RESET ONLY BY
AUTHORIZED PERSON WITH KEY

INDICATOR SHOWS WHEN
ALARM IS TRIPPED

Fig. 8-87. Radar Sentry FR-1 "Footrail" holdup alarm.

Fig. 8-88. Sylvania's basic home protection system.

being occupied. It can be triggered by a hidden pushbutton or a tiny portable remote control transmitter unit that can be carried anywhere. The housewife can carry it in her pocket, or keep it by her bed where it is handy in case of trouble. In a retail store, the transmitter can be carried in the clerk's or proprietor's pocket, or the system can be triggered by push-button or foot pedal installed near the cash register, or under the counter. As a holdup alarm, the HA-1 can be used with the CS-1 telephone alarm (Fig. 8-83) to alert the police without the would-be thief's knowledge. As a prowler alarm, it rings a loud, nerve-shattering bell.

Another holdup alarm is available, the FR-1 Footrail (Fig. 8-87). The housing is made from rugged cast aluminum, and is finished in an attractive wrinkle finish. The FR-1 has been designed to minimize the possibility of false alarms, but at the same time to permit unobtrusive operation when needed. A simple upward movement of the toe is all that is needed to operate the alarm. An indicator flag on the footrail locks in when the alarm is tripped. This is invaluable on jobs where more than one footrail is used, since the cause of alarm can be immediately pinpointed. The indicator flag can be reset only by an authorized person with a key.

SYLVANIA'S BURGLAR AND FIRE ALARM SYSTEM

Sylvania offers a very basic system designed especially for the do-it-yourself installer. The basic home protection kit consists of a control center, sensor mat, alarm bell, fire sensor, handbook, and a hardware kit which includes 100 feet of wire, staples and screws (See Fig. 8-88). The wire is used to connect the sensor mat, alarm bell and fire sensor to the control center. The voltage source consists of four "D" cell flashlight batteries (batteries not supplied). Furthermore, various home protection accessory items may be added to the system, such as remote alarm switches, door and window switches, connectors, authorized entry switches, additional fire sensors, buzzers, and hardware packages. To illustrate the simplicity of the system, excerpts from Sylvania's hand-book follow.

INSTALLATION TABLE

GENERAL INSTRUCTIONS	DETAILED INSTRUCTIONS
I. Control Center	
A. Remove front cover. 	*Insert a small coin or screwdriver in slot located at bottom of the control center. Twist the coin and the front control center will pop out for easy access to battery and accessory terminals.*
B. Mount control center on wall.	*Use three mounting screws provided and mount the control center on a flat surface. The control center can be used as a template by holding it in the desired location and by marking the mounting holes before drilling.*

155

II. Sensor Mat

A. Connect wire of sensor mat using a square knot splice.

3/4"

1. Take one end of the furnished wire and, using a pocketknife or wire cutters, separate about 3" of the two wires from each other.

2. Remove (strip) about 1-1/2" of insulating material from both wires of the separated wire.

3. Strip 1-1/2" of insulating material from the two wires connected to the sensor mat.

4. Connect the two wires to the stripped sensor mat wires as follows:

   a. Tie one of the stripped wires and a sensor mat wire in a square knot splice, ensuring the square knot is such that the insulating materials of the two wires are no more than 3/4" from each other.

   b. Secure the square knot by pulling tightly on each wire in the opposite direction.

   c. Securely wrap the excess strands of the spliced knot around the uninsulated wire.

   d. Wrap insulated tape around the knotted splice.

5. Connect the other wire and the sensor mat wire to each other by repeating step 4a through d.

6. Place the sensor mat on the floor ensuring the connection is toward the wall.

B. Run the wire to the control center and connect it to the SENSOR terminals.

1. Run wire to the control center by running it along the base of the wall and, if necessary, around the door and window frames utilizing the staples provided in the hardware kit.

2. Allow 6" of wire to make connection to the control center. Cut the wire and use a pocketknife to separate about 3" of the two wires from each other.

3. Strip 3/4" of insulating material from each half.

4. Insert the stripped wires through the opening located in the back of the control center and connect both stripped wires to the SENSOR terminals in the following manner:

   a. Remove a nut and washer from each of the two sensor terminal posts.

   b. Tightly wrap one wire clockwise around each sensor terminal post.

   c. Replace a washer and nut on the terminal posts and secure against the wrappings.

III. Alarm Bell

A. Check and mount bell. Use #6 woodscrews and connect wire to bell terminals by bringing the wire through the opening in the back. (See Figures)

1. During shipment and/or handling, the alarm bell striker may slip out of adjustment. Therefore, prior to installation of the alarm bell, check to see that the striker is at rest approximately 1/16 to 1/8 of an inch from the striker plate (See Figure a). If spacing is not correct, loosen adjustment screw and adjust as required.

2. Remove bell dome by removing screw from center of dome.

3. Take one end of the wire and separate 3" of the two wires from each other.

4. Strip 3/4" of insulating material from each wire.

5. Connect the wire to the bell terminals by bringing the wires through the large opening in the back of the bell plate and directly to the two terminals (See Figure b). (Front View, dome removed).

6. Secure the bell assembly in the desired location using wood screws.

7. Replace bell dome with bell dome screw, ensuring that the "TOP" of the bell dome is in the proper position.

B. Run the wire to the control center and connect it to the ALARM terminals.

1. Run the wire to the control center. Be sure the switch is in the OFF position.

2. Allow 6" for connecting the wire to the control center. Cut the wire and separate about 3" of the two wires from each other.

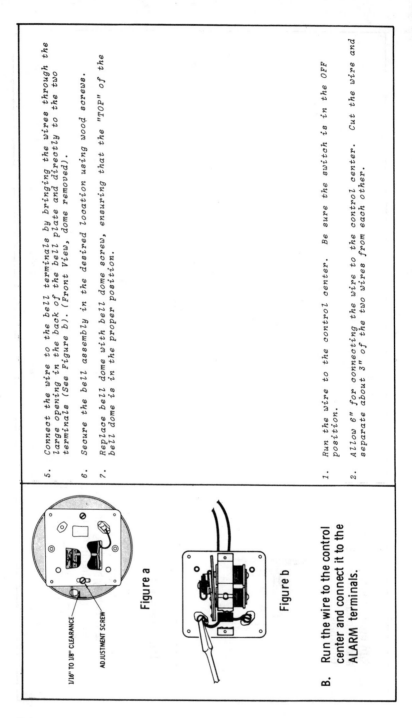

1/16" TO 1/8" CLEARANCE

ADJUSTMENT SCREW

Figure a

Figure b

3. Strip 3/4" of insulating material from each wire.

4. Insert the stripped wires through the back of the control center.

5. Connect one stripped wire, wrapping in a clockwise direction, to each of the ALARM terminals.

6. Tighten the screws that secure the control center to the flat surface.

IV. Testing Installation

A. Place four "D" cell flashlight batteries in the control center and test the alarm system.

1. Place four "D" cell flashlight batteries into the battery holder, ensuring they are properly oriented as per markings in control center.

2. Set switch to TEST.

3. Instruct someone to walk across the sensor mat and observe the test lamp for brightness.

   a. If lamp is bright, the batteries are fresh and are placed correctly in the control center.

   b. If the lamp is dim, assure batteries are correctly oriented. If they are correctly oriented and lamp is still dim, replace the batteries.

   c. If there is no test light, check for proper placement of the batteries and ensure the connections are secure. If batteries are properly placed and connections are secure, replace batteries.

4. Reset switch to OFF.

5. Replace front cover on control center.

6. To test the alarm bell, set the switch to ON.

7. Instruct someone to walk across the sensor mat.

8. Set the switch to OFF in order to turn the alarm bell off.

B. Cover the sensor mat with a throw rug or install under a carpet.

Cover the sensor mat with a throw-rug to make the mat as inconspicuous as possible.

V. Fire Sensor

A. Connect wire to fire sensor and secure sensor to flat surface.

1. Take one end of the furnished wire and, using a pocketknife or wire cutters, separate about 3" of the two wires from each other.

2. Remove (strip) about 3/4" of insulating material from both wires of the separated wires.

3. Insert the wire through either one of the two openings located on the bottom of the fire sensor.

4. Unscrew two terminal screws to maximum height and wrap the wires clockwise around the terminals.

5. Secure terminal screws against wire wrappings.

6. Use two screws provided and mount fire sensor in the desired area.

B. Run the wire to the control center and connect to the terminals.

1. Run the wire to the control center by running it along the base of the wall and, if necessary, around the door and window frames, utilizing the staples provided in the hardware kit.

2. Allow 6" of wire to make connection to the control center. Cut the wire and use a pocketknife to separate about 3" of the two wires from each other.

3. Strip 3/4" of insulating material from each wire.

4. Insert the stripped wires through the opening located in the back of the control center and connect the stripped wires to the terminals in the following manner:

   a. Remove a nut and washer from the right-hand SENSOR terminal post.

   b. Remove a nut and washer from the right-hand ALARM terminal post.

   c. Tightly wrap one wire clockwise around each terminal post.

   d. Replace washers and nuts on terminal posts and secure against wire wrappings.

   Note: Additional nuts and washers can be stacked on terminal posts.

   e. Check for proper operation by heating metal disc in fire sensor with a small flame or other heat source. The alarm can be shut off by removing one of the batteries in the control center.

GENERAL INSTRUCTIONS	DETAILED INSTRUCTIONS
VI. Using the Home Protection System.	
A. To make the Home Protection System operative, set the switch to ON.	*When you retire for the night or leave the house, set the switch to ON. Set the control center to OFF when it is desired to have the Home Protection System inoperative. Replace batteries every six months.*
B. The fire sensors cannot be turned OFF by the switch.	*Continuous protection is provided by this feature as long as the remainder of this system is in proper operating condition. Replace batteries every six months.*

The sensor mat is sensitive to weight. When someone steps on it, it stimulates the control center which in turn causes the bell to ring. Fresh batteries will sound the alarm bell for 15 continuous minutes, unless turned off. To turn the ringing alarm off, merely set the switch to off. The fire sensor will sound the alarm when it reaches a dangerous temperature. The home protection kit is, therefore, capable of providing around-the-clock burglary and fire protection.

The outside cover of the sensor mat is constructed of washable vinyl. Within the mat is a switch which activates the control center to send a signal to the alarm bell. The sensor mat can be placed in any part of the home. It conveniently fits under a throw rug or a carpet.

The control center consists of a test lamp, a 3-position switch for testing the control center and for turning the control center on or off, a solid-state device which activates the alarm bell from the sensor mat, and four "D" cell flashlight batteries, which supply the operating power for the system.

The condition of the batteries can be easily checked by setting the control center switch to the test position. With someone stepping on the mat, a bright glow of the test lamp indicates the batteries are good, a dim glow of the test lamp indicates the batteries should be replaced. The system only consumes power when the alarm bell is ringing.

The alarm bell is designed to operate in normal outside temperatures within the United States. It is coated with a special finish which will withstand normal outside environment when protected from the direct effects of the elements. The alarm bell can be easily mounted on a flat surface.

To install the basic home protection kit, it is first necessary to determine five locations:

(1) Where to locate the sensor mat;

(2) Where to locate the control center;

(3) Where to locate the alarm bell;

(4) Where to locate the wire;

(5) Where to locate the fire sensor.

The following procedures are recommended for maximum security of the home, although numerous variations based on individual circumstances can be just as effective. In addition, placement of accessories should be considered at this time in order to be able to optimize the detection effectiveness with a minimum of installation effort.

Place the sensor mat in a location which tends to be a high-traffic area in the home and which leads to the rooms that contain the items most likely to be stolen or tampered with, such as a color TV, stereo, silverware, or camera. A hallway may be a desirable location (Fig. 8-89). The best location is that which affords the greatest opportunity of mat actuation by the intruder. It is possible that an intruder can bypass the mat by coming through a door or window which is not protected by the home protection kit. However, thoughtful location of the mat will maximize the probability of detection. If a hallway is used, it is suggested the mat be turned so that the long axis of the mat lies in the same direction as the long axis of the hall for maximum effectiveness.

For easiest access and greatest security, install the control center in an inconspicuous place, such as a closet (Fig. 8-90) or behind a door so that an intruder would not be able to readily detect it. Ensure that it is out of the reach of children so that they cannot tamper with it. Also try to locate the control center where it will provide minimum wire run.

Fig. 8-89. The sensor mat should be located in a high-traffic area.

Fig. 8-90. The control center should be located in a closet or other out-of-the-way area.

Place the alarm bell under an eave, over a high door or window frame which may be a convenient exit to the wire, or some other location which is reasonably protected from weather. Also, locate it where it can be readily heard. Locating the alarm bell at the top of the roof peak, utilizing the attic vent as an outlet for the wire, is considered a good location. Locate the bell near a cooperative neighbor, who would call local authorities in an emergency. If you believe the bell has a deterrent effect, mount it in a conspicuous place, but one which is inaccessible to a would-be burglar (Fig. 8-91).

The overall objectives in running the wire are to keep it as short as possible and to keep it inconspicuous. This can be achieved by running the wire along the base of the wall, by pushing it under the edge of the carpet with a screwdriver, or by running it around door and window frames using the staples provided. The wire can be run to the outside by running it through the top of the door, a vent, or even by drilling a small hole in the ceiling through which the wire can pass. Do not, however, run the wire parallel with the television antenna lead as it may create "ghosts" on the TV set. Also do not run it parallel with existing house wiring.

When installing the alarm bell and fire sensor wires, limit their individual lengths to a maximum of 50 feet when using the 24 gauge wire furnished; heavier wire is required if longer runs are necessary. The fire sensor wire length may exceed the 50 feet maximum only if the alarm bell wire length does not exceed its maximum. The combined total wire length of the alarm bell and fire sensor wires must not exceed 100 feet. For example: If 25 feet of wire is used for the alarm bell, then a maximum of 75 feet can be used for the fire sensor.

It is recommended the fire sensor be placed on the ceiling in the rooms containing the water heater or the furnace. Also, because rising heat has a tendency to accumulate at the ceiling near the walls, it is recommended that the sensors **not** be placed any closer than 18 inches from the corners. The sensors are sensitive enough to detect abnormal heat temperatures within a 20-by-20-foot area.

Once the locations of the various components (Fig. 8-92) have been determined, install them in accordance with the accompanying installation tables. Some experienced do-it-yourselfers may be able to complete the installation using only the General Instructions column of the tables. Many installers will want to make use of the step-by-step procedure given in the Detailed Instructions column of the tables in order to eliminate any chance of error.

Fig. 8-91. The alarm bell should be mounted in an inaccessible location.

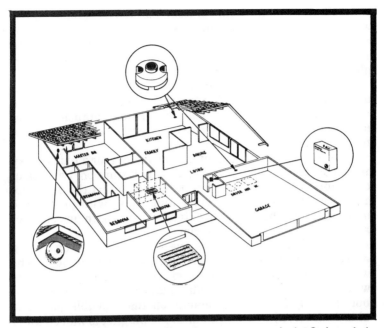

Fig. 8-92. Suggested location for components in Sylvania's home protection system.

In addition to the basic home protection kit, various accessory items may be obtained which will further improve the protection of your home. Also, additional fire sensors can be added to the basic home protection kit which will add increased fire detection capability to your home, and other items can be added for further protection. All of the home protection kit accessories are designed to be connected to the same control center and alarm bell which comes with the basic home protection kit.

The list of accessories available includes remote alarm switches, authorized entry switches, door and window switches, additional fire sensors, alarm buzzers, additional wire, and wire splice connectors. Installation instructions are provided with each accessory item.

The remote alarm switch permits activating the alarm bell manually by momentarily pressing the switch; this will frighten away intruders and summon help from the neighborhood in times of emergency. It can be kept on the night stand near the bedside, for example. It may be especially useful for those who are sick, aged, incapacitated or by those who are living alone. More than one remote alarm switch may be installed within the home or apartment. The remote alarm switch wiring connects to the sensor terminals in the control center. However, if the desired location is closer to a sensor mat wire leading to the control center, the switch wire can be spliced to the sensor mat wire.

The hardware kit provides 100 feet of 24-gauge, 2-conductor wire for connecting the accessory items to the basic home protection kit and relocating existing components. Included are wire staples for dressing the wire against window and door frames, baseboards, flooring, etc.

The connector set includes six connectors for a quick, easy method of splicing wires. No stripping of insulation, twisting of conductors, or taping is required. Simply insert the wire into the receptacles of the connector and crimp with pliers. The connectors can be used to extend wire length or connect branch lines to a main wire run.

The door-window switches are easily mounted on sliding patio doors as well as on conventional doors and windows. The switch consists of a switch portion and a magnet portion; the switch portion mounts on the stationary part of the window or door, the magnet portion mounts on the movable part and holds the internal switch open until the magnet is moved away from the switch by opening the window or door.

The alarm buzzer may be used as an alternate choice to the alarm bell. This is especially useful to apartment dwellers who cannot install the alarm bell outside and prefer not to have an extremely loud alarm in their apartments. However, the buzzer is loud enough to be heard readily by neighboring apartment dwellers. The buzzer connects to the same terminals in the control center as the alarm bell and should be located within three feet of the control center.

Additional fire sensors are available to extend your fire detection capability. The fire sensor senses high temperatures and covers approximately a 20-by-20-foot area. Typical locations for the sensors are in furnace rooms, water heater closets, kitchens, garages, attics and other areas of possible fire hazards.

When installing the fire sensors, it is imperative to note the wire length limitations specified previously. In most cases, this will not present a problem. However, if more than 100 feet of wire is needed, it is recommended that a different wire gauge be used. The table provides information on the maximum distance allowed for a particular wire gauge. Also, any number of parallel connections can be run to the control center. However, it must be emphasized that no one run, plus the length of wire from the control center to the alarm bell, may exceed 100 feet unless a different wire gauge is used. (See table.)

Wire Size	Length of Wire to Furthest Fire Sensor and Length of Alarm Bell Wire
20 gauge, 2-conductor	150 to 250 feet
22 gauge, 2-conductor	100 to 150 feet
24 gauge, 2-conductor	up to 100 feet

TRINE MANUFACTURING CORP.

Trine electric door openers are designed to work in conjunction with various lock sets and to meet the varying conditions of door stiles and jambs. Trine locks are installed in place of the lock "strike." By pushing the release button the door can be opened without a key, but a key can be used to open the lock as before. Figs. 8-93 through 8-95 illustrate several types available. Standard door openers operate on 8 to 16v AC or 3 to 6v DC, using Trine No. 104 10v-5w transformers. For long wire runs, Trine No. 119 (16v-10w) transformers are recommended.

SUMMARY

Whether your interest is one of protecting your own business premises or domicile, this book should provide you with all you need to know about the systems that are currently available and how to adapt them to your own particular needs and requirements. Hopefully, however, there's another type of reader, one with sufficient business acumen to realize the potential available in going into the business of selling, installing and servicing such systems. Right now, in this unsettled time in our nation's history, there is a mass of people who are coming to the conclusion that study and preparation for a career, and the pursuit of that career, is too restrictive of time more properly spent in the wanton pursuit of pleasure. Instead of a nation of ants, struggling to obtain vital needs, this element is changing us to a nation of fiddle-playing (or more properly, guitar strumming) grasshoppers, concerned only with the pleasures of the moment, with no thought for the

Fig. 8-93.

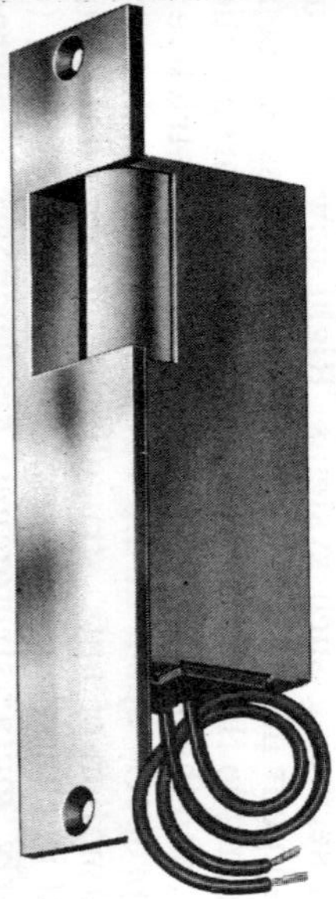

Use Template Drawings before installing.

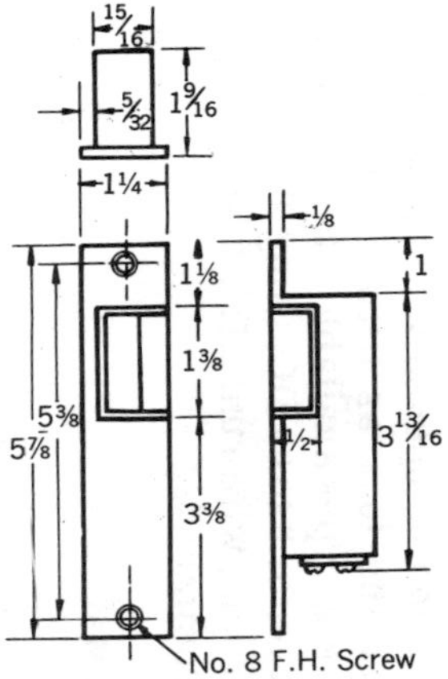

No. 001

(Replaces Trine's famous "Reliance")

MORTISE TYPE

Used with Mortise entrance lock having a latch bolt. Reversible for Right or Left Hand Doors.

NEW, SHALLOW, 1⅝" maximum depth (Ideal for narrow metal door stiles)

Standard, full size **SOLID BRASS** Face Plate, to replace "Reliance" and other makes.

New, stronger electro-mechanical interior with heavy duty coils. 6" wire leads.

CASE & PARTS:	SOLID BRASS
FACE:	STEEL, HEAVY GAUGE
ELECTRO-MAGNETS:	COPPER WIRE
LATCH:	EXTRUDED BRASS,
SIZE:	5⅞" H x 1¼" W x 1⅝" D

No. 001 Satin Brass Finish (US4)

No. 001C Satin Chromium Plated (US26D)

No. 8 F.H. Screw

Patents Pending

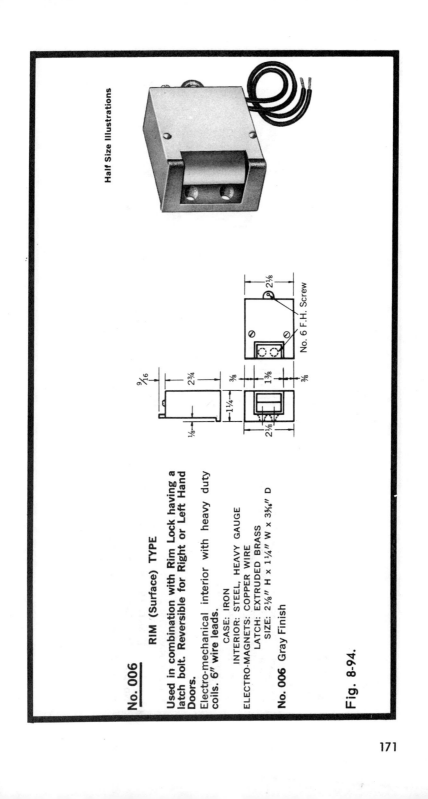

Half Size Illustrations

No. 006

RIM (Surface) TYPE

Used in combination with Rim Lock having a latch bolt. Reversible for Right or Left Hand Doors.

Electro-mechanical interior with heavy duty coils. 6" wire leads.

CASE: IRON
INTERIOR: STEEL, HEAVY GAUGE
ELECTRO-MAGNETS: COPPER WIRE
LATCH: EXTRUDED BRASS
SIZE: 2⅛" H x 1¼" W x 3⅛₆" D

No. 006 Gray Finish

No. 6 F.H. Screw

Fig. 8-94.

171

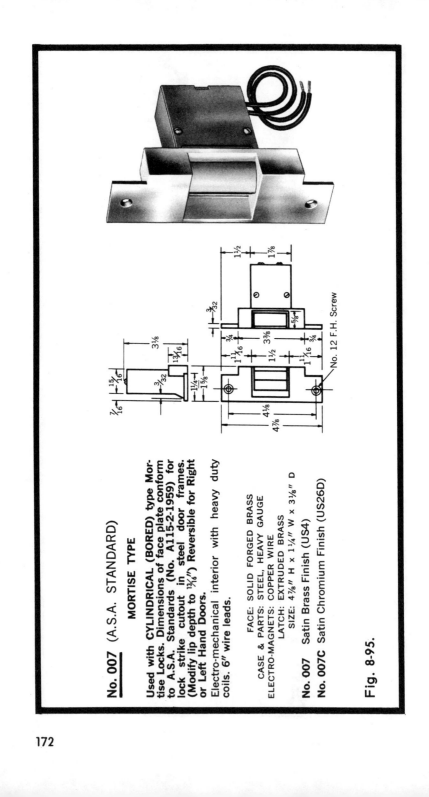

No. 007 (A.S.A. STANDARD)

MORTISE TYPE

Used with CYLINDRICAL (BORED) type Mortise Locks. Dimensions of face plate conform to A.S.A. Standards (No. A115-2-1959) for lock strike cutout in steel door frames. (Modify lip depth to ¹³⁄₁₆") Reversible for Right or Left Hand Doors.

Electro-mechanical interior with heavy duty coils. 6" wire leads.

FACE: SOLID FORGED BRASS
CASE & PARTS: STEEL, HEAVY GAUGE
ELECTRO-MAGNETS: COPPER WIRE
LATCH: EXTRUDED BRASS
SIZE: 4⅞" H x 1¼" W x 3⅛" D

No. 007 Satin Brass Finish (US4)

No. 007C Satin Chromium Finish (US26D)

Fig. 8-95.

hard winter to follow. These would-be grasshoppers demand reward for no effort, and condemn the very "establishment" whose fruits they would like to share. And when the establishment asks them to work, they refuse. Yet, they say, we must live, and so they take.

Since you bought this book, chances are that you did so with money that was earned by you, from your own toils and labors. It was bought just as all your other possessions were bought, and it is those very possessions that you want to protect. This book tries to show you how. Yet, an author, at the very close of a book, always wonders if he has told all that needs to be told and has provided all the required information. If you have any questions, please write the author in care of the publisher, with the assurance that all of your questions will be answered.

List of Manufacturers

Advanced Devices Laboratory
316 Mathew St.
Santa Clara, Calif. 95050

American District Telegraph Co.
155 Sixth Ave.
New York, N.Y. 10013

Alarmtronics Engineering, Inc.
154 California St.
Newton, Mass. 02195

Arrowhead Enterprises, Inc.
P.O. Box 191
Diamond Ave.
Bethel, Conn. 06801

Artronix Surveillance
716 Hanley Industrial Court
St. Louis, Mo. 63144

Ballistics Control Corp.
39-50 Crescent St.
Long Island City, N.Y. 11101

Bourns Security Systems, Inc.
681 Old Willets Path
Smithtown, N.Y. 11787

Concord Electronics Corp.
1935 Armacost Ave.
Los Angeles, Calif. 90025

Detex Corp.
53 Park Place
New York, N.Y. 10007

Electronics Locator Corp.
350 Gotham Parkway
Carlstadt, N.J. 07072

Heath Co.
Benton Harbor, Mich. 49022

Holmes Electric Protective Co.
370 Seventh Ave.
New York, N.Y. 10001

Multi-Elmac Co.
21470 Coolidge Highway
Oak Park, Mich. 48237

Pyrotronics, Inc.
8 Ridgedale Ave.
Cedar Knolls, N.J. 07927

Radar Devices Mfg. Corp.
22003 Harper Ave.
St. Clair Shores, Mich. 48080

Sylvania
730 Third Avenue
New York, N.Y. 10017

Trine Manufacturing Corp.
1430-42 Ferris Place
Bronx, N.Y. 10461

INDEX